b) They make it more difficult for pathogens to survive *[1 mark]* as they out-compete the pathogens for vital resources *[1 mark]*.

2 How to grade your answer:

Level 0: There is no relevant information. ***[No marks]***

Level 1: There is an attempt to describe how the physical defences of the human body act as a barrier to pathogens. The points made are basic and not linked together. ***[1 to 2 marks]***

Level 2: There is a description and some explanation of how the physical defences of the human body act as a barrier to many different pathogens. Some of the points made are linked together. ***[3 to 4 marks]***

Level 3: There is a full and clear description and explanation of how the physical defences of the human body act as a barrier to many different pathogens. The points made are well-linked and the answer has a clear and logical structure. ***[5 to 6 marks]***

Here are some points your answer may include:
The respiratory system is lined with mucus and cilia.
The mucus traps particles that may contain pathogens and the cilia move the mucus to the back of the throat where it can be swallowed.
This helps to prevent infection by pathogens that are breathed in. The skin acts as a barrier to pathogens.
If there is a cut in the skin, platelets clump together to plug the wound.
This is known as blood clotting and it helps to prevent pathogens from entering the bloodstream through cuts.
These physical barriers are non-specific and so will help to protect the nurse against a variety of different pathogens.

Pages 16-17 — The Human Immune System

Warm-up
false, false, true, true

1 Receptors on white blood cells recognise the antigens on the surface of the pathogen ***[1 mark]***.

2 a) Some white blood cells can engulf pathogens ***[1 mark]***, and the enzymes within the white blood cell then digest the engulfed pathogen, destroying it ***[1 mark]***.

b) Antibodies are produced by white blood cells ***[1 mark]***. They attach to the antigens on the pathogen ***[1 mark]*** and disable it ***[1 mark]*** or target the pathogen for destruction by other white blood cells ***[1 mark]***.

3 a) A ***[1 mark]***

Memory cells are white blood cells which are produced the first time a person is exposed to a pathogen. They stay in the blood ready to fight off future infections by the same pathogen.

b) At the time of the second exposure the body has some memory cells that will recognise the pathogen's antigens ***[1 mark]*** and trigger more antibodies to be made ***[1 mark]***. This means antibodies are produced much more quickly following the second exposure (so the curve is steeper) ***[1 mark]***.

c) The response to the second exposure of the pathogen is so fast that the immune system manages to kill off the pathogen before it has a chance to cause any symptoms ***[1 mark]***.

d) White blood cells are specific to only one type of pathogen ***[1 mark]***, so the memory cells from the previous infection cannot trigger a rapid response to another pathogen ***[1 mark]***. This means the reaction of the immune system is slower and the pathogen has time to cause symptoms of the disease ***[1 mark]***.

Page 18 — Reducin the Spread of Disea

1 a) Growing a mixture of plants on the same patch of land at the same time ***[1 mark]***.

b) E.g. spraying crops with pesticides / fungicides / insecticides ***[1 mark]***.

c) Biological control is when another organism is used to control a pest or pathogen ***[1 mark]***.

2 How to grade your answer:

Level 0: There is no relevant information. ***[No marks]***

Level 1: There is an attempt to discuss the measures which might be taken to limit the spread of hepatitis A and B. The points made are basic and not linked together. ***[1 to 2 marks]***

Level 2: There is some discussion of the measures which might be taken to limit the spread of hepatitis A and B. Some of the points made are linked together. ***[3 to 4 marks]***

Level 3: There is a full and clear discussion of the measures which might be taken to limit the spread of hepatitis A and B and the potential costs and benefits. The points made are well-linked and the answer has a clear and logical structure. ***[5 to 6 marks]***

Here are some points your answer may include:
Individuals may be encouraged to practice simple hygiene methods, such as hand washing, to prevent the spread of hepatitis A.
The spread of hepatitis A may also be reduced by improving the sanitation in the town so that people have access to clean drinking water and a good system for disposing of sewage.
However, there may be a high initial cost of creating sanitary conditions.
Another way to reduce the spread of hepatitis A may be to isolate infected individuals so they are less likely to pass the virus onto others.
To prevent the spread of hepatitis B, individuals might be encouraged to use condoms during sexual intercourse.
People could be vaccinated against hepatitis A and B so that they are less likely to develop either disease.
They would also be less likely to pass the disease on to others, so vaccination would be a benefit to both individuals and to the whole town.
However, the vaccination programme is likely to be expensive.

Page 19 — Vaccinations

Warm-Up
inactive, antigens, immune, white, memory

1 a) Because memory cells in the body would be able to immediately produce antibodies to kill off the mumps pathogens ***[1 mark]***.

b) The virus was weakened so that it wouldn't cause the disease in the people being vaccinated ***[1 mark]***.

c) The large proportion of the population who have been vaccinated against the pathogen won't catch the disease ***[1 mark]***. This means that the people who aren't vaccinated are unlikely to catch the disease because there are fewer people able to pass it on ***[1 mark]***.

d) E.g. many diseases may not be serious enough/affect enough people ***[1 mark]*** to justify spending the large amount of money needed to develop, make and distribute the vaccine ***[1 mark]***.

Chapter B2

Pages 20-21 — Culturing Microorganisms

1 a) E.g. the lack of clear zone suggests that antibiotic B had no impact on bacterial growth in culture 2 ***[1 mark]***. The bacteria in culture 2 may have been resistant to antibiotic B ***[1 mark]***.

b) Antibiotic B is more effective against the bacteria than antibiotic A ***[1 mark]***, so there is a larger clear zone around the disc where the bacteria can't grow ***[1 mark]***.

c) i) mean = (85 + 76 + 12 + 80) ÷ 4
= 253 ÷ 4 = **63** ***[2 marks for correct answer, otherwise 1 mark for 85 + 76 + 12 + 80 = 253]***

ii) E.g. the result is an anomaly / not enough antibiotic used / a lower concentration of antibiotic used. ***[1 mark]***

2 a) Area = πr^2, radius = 5.0 mm (± 0.5 mm)
Area = 3.14 × 5.0^2 = **78.5 mm^2** ***[2 marks for correct answer using radius of 5.0 mm (± 0.5 mm), otherwise 1 mark for radius = 5.0 mm (± 0.5 mm)]***

Make sure you either measure the radius from exactly in the middle of the circle, or that you measure the diameter of the circle and divide it by 2.

b) E.g. sterilise the Petri dish and the agar before using them ***[1 mark]***.

c) E.g. pass the inoculating loop through a hot flame before using it ***[1 mark]***. Work near a Bunsen flame so that microorganisms are drawn away from the culture ***[1 mark]***.

d) The bacteria have not been evenly spread across the agar ***[1 mark]***, so it would be very difficult to calculate the size of clear zones around different antibiotics on the plate ***[1 mark]***.

Pages 22-23 — Non-Communicable Diseases

Warm-Up

false, true, false

1 a) It is something that is associated with an increased likelihood of getting a disease ***[1 mark]***.

b) E.g. drinking too much alcohol ***[1 mark]***.

c) the presence of a particular combination of alleles in a person's genome ***[1 mark]***

2 a) There is not enough information about other lifestyle factors that affect the risk of lung cancer ***[1 mark]***. It is not known whether either of the women have genetic variants that would make them more susceptible to lung cancer ***[1 mark]***.

b) E.g. cardiovascular disease / lung disease/chronic bronchitis ***[1 mark]***

3 a) E.g. people in developing countries may find it more difficult to obtain enough protein in their diet compared to people in developed countries ***[1 mark]***.

b) Eating too much may lead to obesity ***[1 mark]***.
Obesity is a risk factor for type 2 diabetes ***[1 mark]***.

4 a) Patient E ***[1 mark]***, because their BMI value indicates that they are moderately obese ***[1 mark]***.

b) A BMI value can be used to determine whether someone is obese, but obesity is only a risk factor for cardiovascular disease, so it doesn't mean a person will definitely get the disease ***[1 mark]***.

c) Any two from: e.g. a lack of exercise ***[1 mark]***. /
Eating a diet containing too much saturated fat ***[1 mark]***. /
Smoking ***[1 mark]***. / Drinking too much alcohol ***[1 mark]***.

Page 24 — Interpreting Data on Disease

1 a) Change = 115.7 – 150.8 = –35.1
Percentage change = (–35.1 ÷ 150.8) × 100 = **–23.3%**
[2 marks for correct answer, otherwise 1 mark for (–35.1 ÷ 150.8) × 100.]

b) Incidence rate of lung cancer in 1994 = 139 per 100 000
So incidence rate per 25 000 = 139 ÷ 4 = **35 males**
[2 marks for correct answer, otherwise 1 mark for incidence rate in 1994 = 139 per 100 000.]

c) They are positively correlated because they both changed in the same direction ***[1 mark]***.

d) E.g. the sample only includes males ***[1 mark]***, therefore it is not representative of the population of Great Britain as a whole ***[1 mark]***.

Page 25 — Investigating Pulse Rate

1 a)

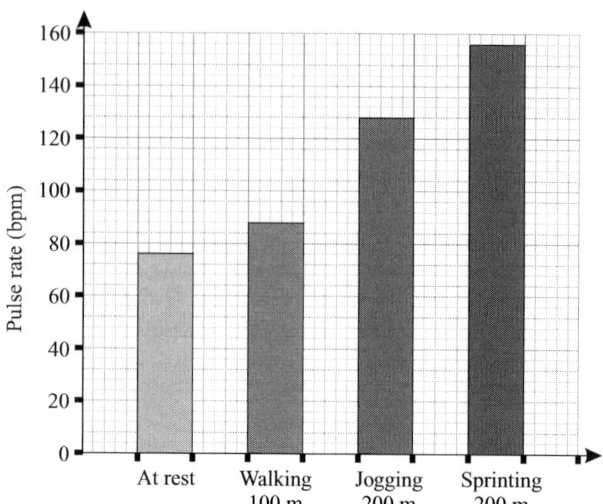

[1 mark for correctly labelled axes, 1 mark for a sensible scale on the y-axis and 1 mark for all bars plotted correctly.]

b) As exercise intensity increased, pulse rate increased ***[1 mark]***.

c) She could measure the time taken for her pulse rate to return to her resting pulse rate after each activity ***[1 mark]***.

d) Any two from: e.g. the same friend that took Lucy's pulse rate should take her classmate's pulse rate ***[1 mark]***. / The classmate should perform the same activities in the same order as Lucy ***[1 mark]***. / The classmate should use the same track/surface to perform the activities as Lucy used ***[1 mark]***.

Page 26 — Treating Disease

1 a) Antiviral drugs are prescribed to treat the viral infection (by stopping the virus from replicating) ***[1 mark]***. Painkillers are prescribed to relieve the pain which results from the infection ***[1 mark]***.

b) Any two from: e.g. any potential adverse reactions to the medication in the patient ***[1 mark]***. / The cost of the medication ***[1 mark]***. / How effective the medication is likely to be in treating the disease in the patient ***[1 mark]***. / Whether the patient could get better without the medication ***[1 mark]***.

2 a) Minor illnesses are likely to clear up on their own, therefore it isn't necessary to prescribe antibiotics ***[1 mark]***. Taking antibiotics will kill non-resistant bacteria in the body ***[1 mark]***, giving resistant strains a competitive advantage ***[1 mark]*** and making them more likely to survive and reproduce ***[1 mark]***.

b) Completing the full course of antibiotics will mean that bacteria with some level of resistance are more likely to be killed ***[1 mark]***, meaning they can't reproduce and become more common in the population ***[1 mark]***.

Chapter B3

Page 27 — Treating Cardiovascular Disease

Warm-Up
blood vessels, coronary heart disease, coronary arteries, fatty material, blood flow

1 a) E.g. have a healthy, balanced diet / reduce saturated fat in his diet ***[1 mark]***.
b) i) E.g. a stent could be inserted into the artery ***[1 mark]*** to keep a narrowed artery open and maintain blood flow to the heart ***[1 mark]***. / A piece of healthy vessel can be taken from elsewhere ***[1 mark]*** to bypass the narrowed artery ***[1 mark]***.
ii) Any two from: e.g. there is a risk of infection. / There is a risk of bleeding. / There is a risk of developing blood clots. / There is a risk that the surgery might not be successful ***[2 marks — 1 mark for each correct answer]***.
c) Any two from: e.g. statins ***[1 mark]***. These reduce the rate of fatty deposits forming in blood vessels ***[1 mark]***. / Anticoagulants ***[1 mark]***. These make blood clots less likely to form ***[1 mark]***. / Antihypertensives ***[1 mark]***. These reduce blood pressure ***[1 mark]***.

Page 28 — Developing New Medicines

1 a) i) cultured human cells and live animals ***[1 mark]***
In preclinical trials, animals are used to test the drug on a whole body or multiple body systems, so the animal needs to be alive. You wouldn't want to test on humans at this stage, just in case the drug proves to be dangerous.
ii) effectiveness / safety ***[1 mark]***
b) doctor only ***[1 mark]***
2 a) He could screen large libraries of chemicals to assess their effectiveness against the target enzyme ***[1 mark]***.
b) i) To check that the drug is safe/doesn't have harmful side effects when the body is working normally ***[1 mark]***.
ii) E.g. it means they will not be given a potential treatment during the trial ***[1 mark]***.

Chapter B3 — Living Together — Food and Ecosystems

Pages 29-30 — Enzymes

1 a) A catalyst increases the rate of a reaction ***[1 mark]***.
b) active site ***[1 mark]***
c) It means usually only one type of substrate will fit into the active site of a specific enzyme ***[1 mark]***.
2 a)

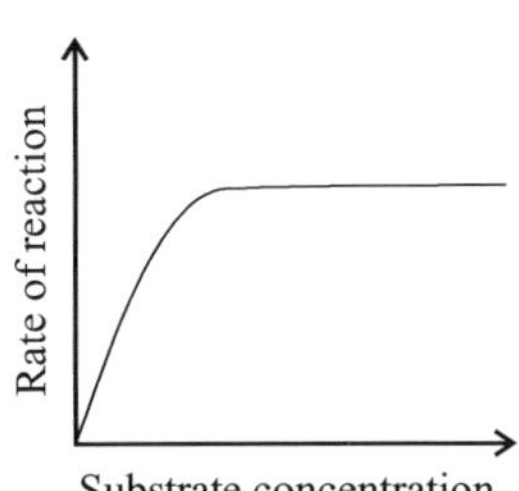

[1 mark]

b) After a certain point, all of the active sites on the enzymes are full ***[1 mark]*** and increasing substrate concentration does not result in more substrate molecules entering the active sites of enzymes, so the rate of the reaction is not affected ***[1 mark]***.
3 At 38 °C Enzyme A will be most active as this is its optimum temperature ***[1 mark]***. At 60 °C, enzyme A is denatured and will not be active ***[1 mark]*** because the shape of the active site has changed and the substrate will no longer 'fit' into the active site ***[1 mark]***.

4 a) i)

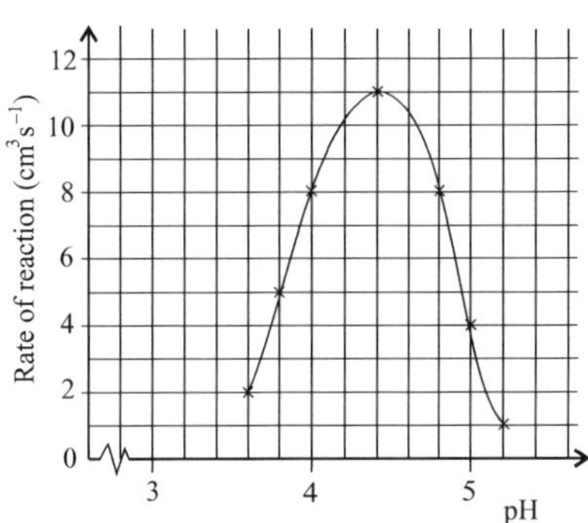

[1 mark for all points correctly plotted, 1 mark for a smooth curve of best fit.]
ii) optimum pH = 4.4 ***[1 mark]***
b) The enzyme activity decreases ***[1 mark]*** because the pH affects the bonds in the enzyme, causing the active site to change shape ***[1 mark]*** and denaturing the enzyme ***[1 mark]***.

Page 31 — More on Enzymes

1 a) 36 °C, as this was the temperature at which the iodine solution stopped turning blue-black first ***[1 mark]***, meaning the starch had been broken down the fastest ***[1 mark]***.
b) E.g. the amylase was denatured by the high temperature, so the starch was not broken down ***[1 mark]***.
c) i) By using a buffer ***[1 mark]***.
ii) Any two from: e.g. the concentration of starch solution / the concentration of amylase / the volume of starch and amylase solution added to the iodine / the volume of iodine solution in the wells ***[2 marks — 1 mark for each correct answer]***.
d) Test the solutions more frequently (e.g. every 10 seconds) ***[1 mark]***.

Pages 32-33 — Photosynthesis

Warm-up
green plants, light, glucose, chlorophyll, chloroplasts

1 a)

	Input	Output(s)
First stage of photosynthesis	1. Light 2. Chlorophyll 3. Water	1. Oxygen gas 2. Hydrogen ions
Second stage of photosynthesis	1. Carbon dioxide gas 2. Hydrogen ions	1. Glucose

[5 marks — 1 mark for each correct answer.]
b) Any two from: e.g. it is used during cellular respiration. / It is converted to and stored as starch. / It is used to make larger molecules such as lipids/proteins/carbohydrates. / It is used to make up the organism's biomass. ***[2 marks — 1 mark for each correct answer.]***
c) Energy is transferred from the environment during the reaction. ***[1 mark]***
2 a) i) Plants produce glucose during photosynthesis and store this glucose as starch ***[1 mark]***. If the leaf had been photosynthesising, it would have contained starch and the iodine solution would have turned blue-black ***[1 mark]***. If the leaf had not been photosynthesising, it would not have contained starch and would not have turned blue-black ***[1 mark]***.
ii) Put the leaf in boiling water to stop any chemical reactions from happening inside the leaf ***[1 mark]***. Then put the leaf in a boiling tube with some ethanol and heat it gently in a water bath to remove any chlorophyll ***[1 mark]***. Rinse the leaf in cold water and add a few drops of iodine solution to test the leaf for starch ***[1 mark]***.

Chapter B3

b) Light is needed to transfer energy to the chlorophyll *[1 mark]*. This energy is then used to split water into oxygen gas and hydrogen ions *[1 mark]*.

c) He could perform the starch test on both the green and white parts of the leaf *[1 mark]*. If only the green part of the leaf contains starch and turns blue-black, it shows that chlorophyll is needed for photosynthesis *[1 mark]*.

Page 34 — Investigating the Rate of Photosynthesis

1 a) oxygen *[1 mark]*

b) $1.2 \div 2 =$ **0.6 cm³/h** *[1 mark]*

c) i) As the distance from the lamp increases, the rate of gas production decreases *[1 mark]*. This is because the intensity of the light reaching the plant decreases as the flask is placed further away *[1 mark]*, and light intensity is a limiting factor for photosynthesis *[1 mark]*.

ii) E.g. by repeating the experiment with more distances from the light source / at greater distances from the light source *[1 mark]*.

d) Different lamps may produce different intensities of light *[1 mark]*, so using the same lamp helps to ensure that the distance between the lamp and the flask is the only thing affecting the light intensity *[1 mark]*.

Pages 35-36 — Limiting Factors of Photosynthesis

1 a) inverse square law *[1 mark]*

b) The light intensity reaching the plant would be four times greater *[1 mark]*.

The inverse square law is light intensity $\propto 1/d^2$. This means that as the square of the distance decreases, light intensity increases proportionally — in other words, if you halve the distance, the light intensity will be four times greater.

2 a) The rate of photosynthesis increases between points A and B *[1 mark]*. This is because increasing the temperature (up to the optimum) increases the rate at which the enzymes involved in photosynthesis work *[1 mark]*.

b) Increasing the temperature after point B causes the rate of photosynthesis to fall *[1 mark]*. This is because the temperatures are too high for the enzymes involved in photosynthesis to work *[1 mark]*. At point C, no photosynthesis is occurring because all the enzymes are denatured *[1 mark]*.

3 a) At first, as the carbon dioxide concentration increases, the rate of photosynthesis increases as well *[1 mark]*. Then, at 0.10 arbitrary units of carbon dioxide, the graph flattens out / after 0.10 arbitrary units of carbon dioxide, as the carbon dioxide concentration increases, the rate of photosynthesis no longer increases *[1 mark]*.

b) E.g. increase the temperature *[1 mark]*, increase the light intensity *[1 mark]*.

c)

Rate of photosynthesis (arbitrary units)

Light intensity (arbitrary units)

[1 mark for correctly labelled axes, 1 mark for correctly sketched line.]

Page 37 — Diffusion, Osmosis and Active Transport

Warm-up

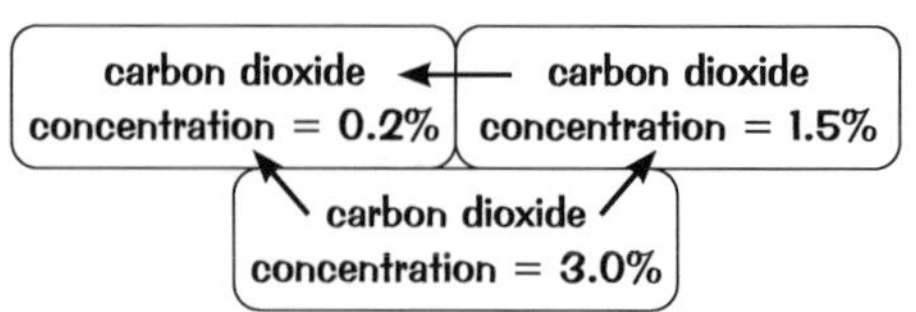

Diffusion is when molecules move down a concentration gradient, from an area with a higher concentration to an area with a lower concentration. So each of the arrows in the diagram should be moving from a cell with a higher concentration of CO_2 to one with a lower concentration of CO_2.

1 a) water *[1 mark]*, partially permeable *[1 mark]*, higher *[1 mark]*, lower *[1 mark]*

b) A plant is absorbing water from the soil *[1 mark]*.

2 a) ⟶ *[1 mark]*

b) ⟶ *[1 mark]*

c) ⟵ *[1 mark]*

For this question you need to work out the relative concentration of the molecules on each side of the membrane and read the question carefully to see what process is involved in their movement.

Page 38 — Transport in Plants and Prokaryotes

1 a) stomata *[1 mark]*

b) Carbon dioxide diffuses into the leaf *[1 mark]*. Water vapour diffuses out of the leaf *[1 mark]*. Oxygen diffuses out of the leaf *[1 mark]*.

c) Gases diffuse from air spaces inside the leaf into the plant cells *[1 mark]* across the cells' partially permeable outer membranes *[1 mark]*.

2 a) To make proteins *[1 mark]*.

b) The concentration of nitrate ions is higher inside the plant cells than in the soil (outside the plant cells) *[1 mark]*, so the nitrate ions would move out of the plant cells by diffusion *[1 mark]*.

c) The roots would absorb fewer nitrate ions *[1 mark]* because there would be less ATP to provide the energy needed to actively transport the ions through the cell membrane and into the root *[1 mark]*.

Pages 39-40 — Investigating Diffusion and Osmosis

1 a) To allow him to compare the effects of the sucrose concentrations on eggs that didn't have the same initial mass *[1 mark]*.

b) The water concentration was lower inside the eggs than in the solution in the beaker *[1 mark]*, so the eggs gained mass as water was drawn into them by osmosis *[1 mark]*.

c)

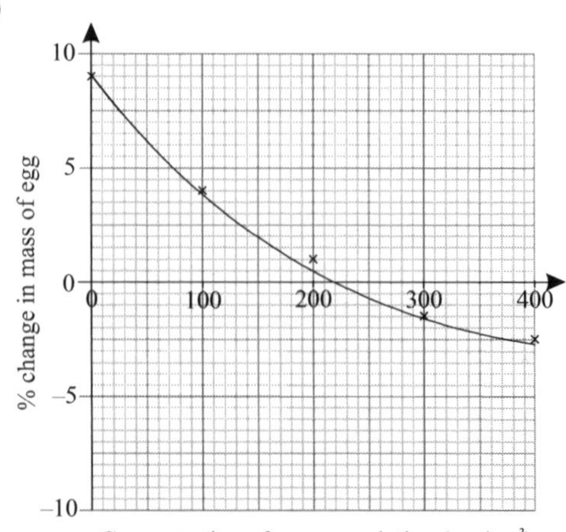

[1 mark for correctly plotting the data, 1 mark for labelling the axes correctly, 1 mark for choosing a sensible scale, 1 mark for drawing a smooth curve of best fit.]

Chapter B3

d) 220 mg/cm^3 ($\pm$ 10 mg/cm^3) ***[1 mark]***

To work out the concentration of fluid inside the eggs you need to look for the point at which your line of best fit cross the x-axis. This is the point at which there is no change in mass and therefore no movement of water by osmosis — so the concentration of fluid inside the eggs and the sucrose solution must be the same.

2 a) A change in pH ***[1 mark]***.

b) Increasing the concentration of ammonia increases the rate of diffusion ***[1 mark]***.

c) E.g. the volume of the ammonia drops ***[1 mark]***, which could have been controlled by measuring them with a dropping pipette ***[1 mark]***. / The size of the litmus paper ***[1 mark]*** which could have been controlled by measuring the length and width of the strip with a ruler ***[1 mark]***. / The distance the ammonia had to travel ***[1 mark]***, which could have been controlled by making sure the distance between the cotton wool and litmus paper was the same each time ***[1 mark]***.

d) i) E.g. estimating the point at which the litmus paper has changed colour ***[1 mark]***.

ii) E.g. by repeating the experiment and calculating a mean ***[1 mark]***.

Page 41 — Xylem and Phloem

Warm-up

transpiration, evaporation, leaves, transpiration stream, roots, translocation, sugars

1 a) i) phloem ***[1 mark]***

ii) To transport food substances (mainly sugars) up and down the stem from photosynthetic to non-photosynthetic tissues/to growing and storage tissues ***[1 mark]***. / To enable translocation ***[1 mark]***.

b) i) The xylem have thick, stiff cellulose walls strengthened by lignin ***[1 mark]*** which give the plant support ***[1 mark]***.

ii) E.g. the xylem vessels carry water that is being drawn up the stem (from the roots to the leaves) as a result of transpiration ***[1 mark]***.

Page 42 — Stomata

1 a) X: stomata ***[1 mark]***
Y: guard cells ***[1 mark]***

b) They are responsible for opening and closing stomata ***[1 mark]***, in order to control gas exchange and water loss from a leaf ***[1 mark]***.

c) Paint thin layers of clear nail varnish onto a leaf ***[1 mark]***. Place clear sticky tape onto the painted leaf and use it to peel the varnish off. The varnish will have an impression of the leaf's surface ***[1 mark]***. Stick the tape onto a microscope slide for viewing ***[1 mark]***.

2 a) Leaf A = (25.2 + 20.1 + 18.7 + 17.9) ÷ 4 = **20.5 µm** (3 s.f.) ***[1 mark]***
Leaf B = (14.7 + 12.8 + 14.1 + 13.2) ÷ 4 = **13.7 µm** (3 s.f.) ***[1 mark]***

b) Leaf B ***[1 mark]*** because stomata begin to close when light intensity decreases / stomata open more as light intensity increases ***[1 mark]***. This means the leaf with the lower mean stomatal diameter (leaf B) will have had the measurements taken in conditions of lower light intensity ***[1 mark]***.

Page 43 — Transpiration Rate

1 a) (0.92 – 1.35) ÷ 1.35 x 100 = **31.9%** ***[2 marks for the correct answer or 1 mark for correct working]***

b) i) As air flow increases, loss of mass increases ***[1 mark]***.

ii) Air flow causes water vapour around the leaf to be swept away, creating a lower concentration of water outside the leaf ***[1 mark]***. This causes water to diffuse out of the leaf faster (from an area of higher concentration to an area of lower concentration), so the plant loses mass ***[1 mark]***.

c) E.g. they could place a shoot next in a darkened room/ cupboard and one next to a lamp ***[1 mark]***. / They could place shoots next to lamps that emit different light intensities ***[1 mark]***.

Page 44 — Using a Potometer

1 a)

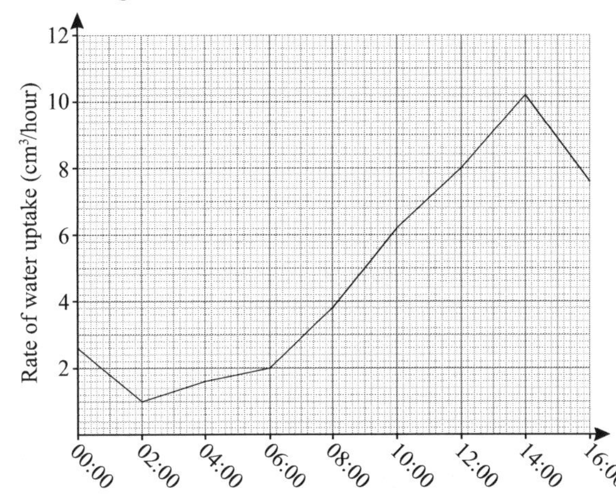

[1 mark for using a sensible scale for the y-axis, 1 mark for labelling the y-axis, 1 mark for accurately plotting the points, 1 mark for connecting the points with straight lines through the centre of each point.]

It might sound a bit obvious, but make sure you always use a sharp pencil to draw graphs like this. Your graph might turn out inaccurate if your pencil is blunt, which could lose you marks.

b) 5.0 cm^3/hour ***[1 mark]***

c) 5.1 cm^3/hour ***[1 mark]***

d) Any two from: e.g. light intensity increased. / Temperature increased. / Air flow around the leaf improved. ***[2 marks — 1 mark for each correct answer]***.

Pages 45-46 — Ecosystems and Interactions Between Organisms

Warm-Up

A — Moisture level, pH of soil, Temperature, Light intensity, Toxic chemicals

B — Number of predators, Food availability, Number of competitors, Presence of pathogens

1 All the organisms of different species living in a habitat. ***[1 mark]***

2 a) Bioaccumulation ***[1 mark]***

b) It means that the concentration of DDT will have increased at each stage of the food chain ***[1 mark]***.

3 a) E.g. the population of prickly acacia may have increased ***[1 mark]*** because they grow best when there is plenty of water ***[1 mark]***.

b) E.g. the prickly acacia may become distributed over a wider area ***[1 mark]*** as they may spread into areas that were previously too cold for them ***[1 mark]***.

c) E.g. the prickly acacia may compete with the grasses for resources (such as light, water, space and nutrients) causing their populations to decrease ***[1 mark]***.

Chapter B3

4 a) E.g. the populations of roe deer may have increased because their natural predators are extinct / because there was lots of available resources that were not already being exploited ***[1 mark]***. Bigger populations of roe deer may have led to increased competition between the roe deer for resources, e.g. food, shelter ***[1 mark]***, so they may have had to expand their habitat in search of more resources ***[1 mark]***.

b) The population of roe deer would probably decrease ***[1 mark]*** because the lynx will prey on the roe deer ***[1 mark]***.

Pages 47-48 — Investigating Ecosystems

1 a) i) To make sure the sample is representative of the whole area ***[1 mark]***.

ii) E.g. divide the field into a grid and place the quadrats at coordinates selected using a random number generator ***[1 mark]***.

b) 13 buttercups ***[1 mark]***

The mode/modal number is the most frequently occurring number.

c) 15.5 buttercups ***[1 mark]***

To answer this question, simply put the numbers of buttercups in each quadrat in order from the smallest to the largest, like this: 12, 13, 13, 13, 15, 16, 16, 23, 23, 26. The median number is halfway along this list — so it lies halfway between 15 and 16.

d) $15 + 13 + 16 + 23 + 26 + 23 + 13 + 12 + 16 + 13 = 170$
$170 \div 10 = 17$ buttercups per 0.5 m^2 ***[1 mark]***

e) $17 \times 2 = 34$ per m^2
$34 \times 1750 = 59\ 500$ buttercups
[2 marks for the correct answer, otherwise 1 mark for multiplying answer to part d) by 2.]

2 a) $(85 \times 94) \div 6 = 1331.66... =$ **1332 worms** ***[1 mark]***

b) A brightly coloured tag might affect the worms' chances of survival by making them more visible to predators (e.g birds) ***[1 mark]***. This would reduce the worms' population size and so give an inaccurate estimate ***[1 mark]***.

c) So that the population of worms had time to move about / redistribute before the second sampling ***[1 mark]***.

d) E.g. capture the worms over a longer period of time to get a bigger sample. / Repeat the investigation several times and calculate the mean ***[1 mark]***.

e) E.g. that no worms died/were born between the first and second samples. / That marking hasn't affected the worms' chance of survival ***[1 mark]***.

Pages 49-50 — More on Investigating Ecosystems

1 a) i) Spots and stripes ***[1 mark]***

ii) Butterfly F ***[1 mark]***

b) Any two from: e.g. a key with more butterflies included ***[1 mark]***. / A key with higher quality photographs ***[1 mark]***. / A key with colour photographs ***[1 mark]***. / A key with more features listed ***[1 mark]***.

2 a) Zones B and C ***[1 mark]***

b) long grass ***[1 mark]***

c) Zone A is closest to the pond where the soil has more moisture ***[1 mark]***. Zone A also has a higher light intensity ***[1 mark]***.

d) Zone B ***[1 mark]*** because only short grass grows in zone B ***[1 mark]***.

e) E.g. a quadrat could be placed at regular intervals along the transect ***[1 mark]*** and samples taken by estimating the percentage cover of the four different plant types ***[1 mark]***.

Page 51 — Investigating Factors Affecting Distribution

1 a) E.g. the distribution of organisms is affected by abiotic factors such as pH ***[1 mark]***. By recording soil pH at the different quadrat sites, the students can see if there is any evidence that pH is affecting the distribution of the plant species in the area ***[1 mark]***.

b) i) E.g. soil moisture level / light intensity ***[1 mark]***.

ii) E.g. soil moisture meter / light sensor ***[1 mark]***.

2 a) one ***[1 mark]***

b) The further away from the road, the greater the number of lichen species ***[1 mark]*** because the concentration of sulfur dioxide from cars gets lower further from the road ***[1 mark]***.

c) 25 m ***[1 mark]***

Page 52 — Food Chains and Food Webs

1 a) E.g. capybaras are eaten by jaguars. / Biomass is transferred from the capybaras to the jaguars ***[1 mark]***.

Don't get mixed up about the direction of the arrows in food webs and food chains. The arrows show the direction of biomass transfer. So the organism the arrow is pointing from is eaten by the organism the arrow is pointing to, i.e. the capybara is eaten by the jaguar.

b) i) E.g. the population of bats may decrease because there will be less food for them to eat ***[1 mark]***.

ii) E.g. the population of mice may increase because they are not being preyed on by as many bats. / The population of mice may decrease because the bats need more food ***[1 mark]***.

c) Any two from: flowering tree/banana tree/grass ***[2 marks — 1 mark for each correct answer]***.

2 a) The sea otter eats organisms which feed on the kelp ***[1 mark]***, so it is dependent on the kelp to provide food for its prey ***[1 mark]***. The kelp is dependent on the sea otter to keep the numbers of sea snails, sea urchins and crabs down ***[1 mark]***, as they feed on the kelp and would reduce the amount of kelp if their numbers increased by too much ***[1 mark]***.

b) The fish ***[1 mark]*** because according to the food web, crabs are their only source of food ***[1 mark]***.

Page 53 — Making and Breaking Biological Molecules

1 By eating both producers and other consumers ***[1 mark]***.

2 a) A: simple sugars (e.g. glucose) ***[1 mark]***
B: amino acids ***[1 mark]***
C: lipid ***[1 mark]***
D: glycerol ***[1 mark]***

b) Consumers need to be able to break down large molecules into smaller components so that they can be absorbed into the bloodstream and transported to cells ***[1 mark]*** where they can be built up into larger molecules and used to form the biomass of the consumer ***[1 mark]***.

Page 54 — Testing for Biological Molecules

Warm-up
Biuret test — Proteins
Benedict's test — Reducing sugars
Emulsion test — Lipids
Iodine test — Starch

1 a) E.g. add the sample of egg whites to a test tube containing ethanol ***[1 mark]***. Shake the tube for about a minute until the egg whites dissolve ***[1 mark]***. Pour the solution into water ***[1 mark]***. If a milky emulsion forms, then there are lipids present; if not, then no lipids are present ***[1 mark]***.

b) E.g. add some biuret reagent/a few drops of sodium hydroxide and some copper(II) sulfate solution to a sample of the egg whites ***[1 mark]***. If proteins are present, then the solution will turn purple ***[1 mark]*** and if not then the solution will be blue ***[1 mark]***.

2 a) He should add Benedict's reagent to each of the solutions ***[1 mark]***, then heat the test tubes in a water bath that's set to 75 °C ***[1 mark]***. He should then look out for the formation of a coloured precipitate and note the colour if one is formed ***[1 mark]***.

Glucose is a reducing sugar so the Benedict's test can be used to determine the relative concentrations of glucose in the test tubes.

Chapter B4

b)

	Tube 1	Tube 2	Tube 3	Tube 4
substance observed	yellow precipitate	blue solution	red precipitate	green precipitate
glucose concentration (M)	**0.1**	**0**	**1**	**0.02**

[1 mark]

The higher the concentration of glucose in the solution, the further the colour change goes along the following scale: blue — green — yellow — orange — brick red. If no precipitate forms then there are no reducing sugars in the solution.

Page 55 — Cycles in Ecosystems

1 a) E.g. air/soil/fossil fuels/waste ***[1 mark]***

Abiotic just means 'not living' so you can choose anything from the diagram that isn't alive.

b) respiration ***[1 mark]***

c) photosynthesis ***[1 mark]***

d) They release carbon dioxide when they are burned ***[1 mark]***.

e) Animal waste and dead plants and animals are being broken down by decomposers/microorganisms ***[1 mark]***. These decomposers/microorganisms release carbon dioxide back into the air by respiration as they break down the material ***[1 mark]***.

2 The trees have fewer leaves so less photosynthesis will take place ***[1 mark]***. This means that less carbon dioxide will be removed from the air, contributing to a greater concentration of carbon dioxide in the atmosphere in winter ***[1 mark]***.

Page 56 — More on Cycles in Ecosystems

Warm-up

evaporate, water vapour, cools, precipitation, runoff

1 a) A — evaporation ***[1 mark]***
B — precipitation ***[1 mark]***
C — condensation ***[1 mark]***

b) i) When an organism or cell gets rid of the waste products of chemical reactions ***[1 mark]***.

ii) Excretion, e.g. sweating/urination/breathing out ***[1 mark]*** is how animals return water to the environment ***[1 mark]***.

c) Through transpiration ***[1 mark]*** and in their tissues via food chains ***[1 mark]***.

Chapter B4 — Using Food and Controlling Growth

Pages 57-58 — Respiration

1 a) It is an exothermic reaction that transfers energy from the breakdown of glucose ***[1 mark]***.

b) oxygen ***[1 mark]***

2 a) 5.88 ÷ 20 = **0.29 cm³/min** (2 s.f.) ***[1 mark]***

b) Glucose ***[1 mark]*** because this substrate produced the most CO_2 / the rate of respiration was fastest for this substrate ***[1 mark]***.

The more CO_2 produced, the more O_2 is needed to produce it. And a faster rate of respiration means that more O_2 is used up in the same time period.

c) Any two from: e.g. the volume of substrate solution / the concentration of substrate solution / the temperature of the water bath / the amount of yeast added to each test tube ***[2 marks — 1 mark for each correct answer]***.

d) the mitochondria ***[1 mark]***

3 a) E.g. the snail must have enough oxygen for two hours / the snail must not dry out ***[1 mark]***.

b) The glass beads are acting as a control in the experiment ***[1 mark]*** to show that any change in the carbon dioxide concentration of Beaker A is due to the snail and not some other factor ***[1 mark]***.

c) i) The percentage of carbon dioxide in the air has increased over the two hours because the snail releases carbon dioxide as it respires ***[1 mark]***.

ii) It would have decreased ***[1 mark]*** because the snail would have used up oxygen as it respired ***[1 mark]***.

d) The internal temperature of Beaker A would be higher than that of Beaker B / the internal temperature of Beaker A would increase whereas the internal temperature of Beaker B would stay the same ***[1 mark]*** because during respiration energy is transferred to the environment by heat ***[1 mark]***.

Pages 59-60 — More on Respiration

1 a) i) E.g. glucose ***[1 mark]***

ii) oxygen ***[1 mark]***

b) Aerobic respiration has a higher ATP yield/is more efficient than anaerobic respiration ***[1 mark]***.

c) In plants the products of anaerobic respiration are ethanol ***[1 mark]*** and carbon dioxide ***[1 mark]***, whereas in animals the only product is lactic acid ***[1 mark]***.

2 a) anaerobic respiration ***[1 mark]***

b) glucose → ethanol + carbon dioxide
[2 marks, 1 mark for each side of the equation correct]

c) E.g. if the container wasn't sealed tightly, oxygen would be able to enter the container ***[1 mark]***. This could lead to the yeast respiring aerobically, meaning that ethanol/alcohol wouldn't be produced ***[1 mark]***.

3 The root cells of the rice plant will be respiring anaerobically, since the roots are submerged in water (where there is little/no oxygen) ***[1 mark]***. One of the products of anaerobic respiration in plants is ethanol ***[1 mark]***. Therefore it is advantageous for the roots of the rice plants to have a higher tolerance to ethanol to prevent them being poisoned by the ethanol they produce ***[1 mark]***.

4 a) Oxygen consumption increased rapidly at first then increased more slowly ***[1 mark]***, until around 8 minutes when it levelled off ***[1 mark]***.

b) In the final two minutes of exercise, the man's oxygen consumption remained constant ***[1 mark]***. This suggests that his muscles were respiring anaerobically (as well as aerobically) to supply the extra energy needed for his muscles to continue to work harder, as this process doesn't require oxygen ***[1 mark]***.

Page 61 — The Cell Cycle and Mitosis

1 a) The number of subcellular structures is increasing ***[1 mark]***.
The DNA is duplicating ***[1 mark]***.

b) The cytoplasm is dividing ***[1 mark]***.
The cell membrane is dividing ***[1 mark]***.

c) They are genetically identical ***[1 mark]***.

d) So the organism can grow ***[1 mark]***.

e) i) A change (mutation) in one of the genes that controls cell division ***[1 mark]***.

ii) Uncontrolled cell division can result in a mass of abnormal cells called a tumour ***[1 mark]***. Tumours that invade and destroy surrounding tissue are called cancers ***[1 mark]***.

Page 62 — Microscopy

1 a) Cell A is half as wide as Cell B ***[1 mark]***.

b) Cell A has 0.5^2 of the area of Cell B. / Cell A has a quarter of the area of Cell B ***[1 mark]***.

2 a) Electron microscopes have a higher magnification ***[1 mark]*** and a higher resolution than light microscopes ***[1 mark]***.

Chapter B5

b) E.g. smaller structures can be seen under an electron microscope / structures can be seen with greater detail ***[1 mark]***. This has allowed scientists to develop explanations for how the internal structures of, e.g. mitochondria/ chloroplasts, relate to their functions ***[1 mark]***.

3 a) Staining the chromosomes allows them to be seen more clearly ***[1 mark]***.

b) A ***[1 mark]*** because the chromosomes in cell A are spread out/not condensed ***[1 mark]***.

Pages 63-64 — More Microscopy

Warm-up

1

	÷ 1000 will convert to:	× 1000 will convert to:	in standard form, original unit will be:
mm	m	μm	$\times 10^{-3}$ m
μm	**mm**	**nm**	$\times \mathbf{10^{-6}}$ m
nm	**μm**	**pm**	$\times \mathbf{10^{-9}}$ m
pm	**nm**		$\times \mathbf{10^{-12}}$ m

2 Total magnification = **eyepiece lens** magnification × **objective lens** magnification

It doesn't matter which way round you write eyepiece lens and objective lens in the formula.

$$\text{magnification} = \frac{\text{measured size}}{\text{actual size}}$$

1 a) i) Total magnification = eyepiece lens magnification × objective lens magnification
Total magnification = 10 × 100 = **× 1000** ***[1 mark]***

ii) 25 μm ***[1 mark]***

The height of the cells is about 2 and a half times the length of the scale bar.

b) 8×10^{-6} m ***[1 mark]***

2 a) length of cell A in image = 24 mm
magnification = measured size ÷ actual size
= 24 ÷ 0.012 = **× 2000**
[2 marks for correct answer, otherwise 1 mark for length of cell = 24 mm.]

b) measured size = magnification × actual size
400 × 0.012 = **4.8 mm** ***[2 marks for correct answer, otherwise 1 mark for 400 × 0.012.]***

3 a) actual size = measured size ÷ magnification
actual size = 10 mm ÷ 1000 = 0.01 mm
0.01 mm x 1000 = **10 μm** ***[3 marks for correct answer, otherwise 1 mark for 10 ÷ 1000, 1 mark for 0.01 × 1000.]***

b) 4×10^{-5} = 0.00004 mm
0.00004 mm × 1000 = 0.04 μm
0.04 μm × 1000 = **40 nm** ***[3 marks for correct answer, otherwise 1 mark for 0.00004 × 1000, 1 mark for 0.04 × 1000.]***

Page 65 — Sexual Reproduction and Meiosis

1 a) Gametes contain half the number of chromosomes in other body cells. ***[1 mark]***

b) Four genetically different daughter cells. ***[1 mark]***

c) zygote ***[1 mark]***

2 a)

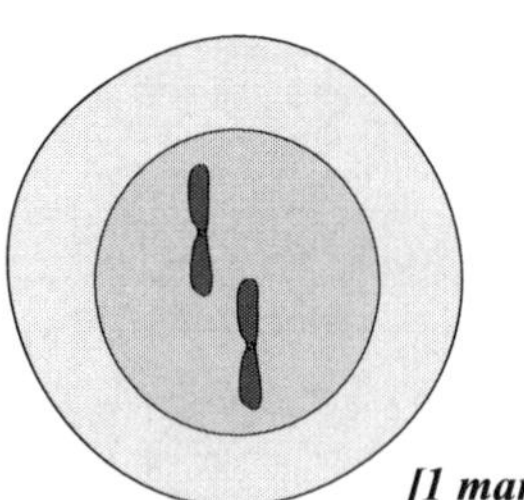

[1 mark]

The left-hand diagram in the question shows a cell containing two pairs of chromosomes just before it undergoes meiosis. The first division causes these pairs to split up so that the two new cells only contain one chromosome from each pair. In the second division the chromosome in each cell is pulled apart so that each of the four gametes end up containing only one chromosome arm.

b) It's needed to produce cells/gametes with half the number of chromosomes in the body cells ***[1 mark]*** so that when two gametes fuse at fertilisation, chromosomes from the mother and father can pair up ***[1 mark]*** and the zygote ends up with the full number of chromosomes ***[1 mark]***.

Page 66 — Stem Cells

Warm-up

differentiate, specialised, early human embryos, growing, any cell type

1 a) i) E.g. embryonic stem cells have the potential to produce any type of cell at all ***[1 mark]***, whereas adult stem cells are less versatile ***[1 mark]***.

ii) E.g. some people think it's wrong to destroy a potential human life ***[1 mark]***.

b) meristem tissue ***[1 mark]***

For this question it's no good writing 'the tips of roots' or 'the tips of shoots' — you've been asked to name the tissue that produces stem cells, not give its location within a plant.

2 a) Switch on the genes that produce insulin/the genes that produce proteins required by an insulin-secreting cell ***[1 mark]***. Switch off any genes which produce proteins that aren't required ***[1 mark]***.

b) E.g. there may be a risk of tumour development ***[1 mark]*** if the rate at which the new insulin-secreting cells divide inside the patient can't be controlled ***[1 mark]***. / There may be a risk of disease transmission from the donor to the recipient ***[1 mark]*** if viruses are present within the embryonic stem cells used to develop the new insulin-secreting cells ***[1 mark]***.

Chapter B5 — The Human Body — Staying Alive

Page 67 — Exchange of Materials

1 a) As a multicellular organism, the stickleback has a relatively small surface area to volume ratio ***[1 mark]***. This means diffusion to and from cells deep within its body is too slow ***[1 mark]***. To speed up the exchange of substances, it needs specialised exchange surfaces to increase its surface area to volume ratio ***[1 mark]*** and a mass transport system to move substances around its body (so substances have a shorter distance to diffuse) ***[1 mark]***.

b) These organisms would have a relatively large surface area to volume ratio ***[1 mark]*** so oxygen would be able to diffuse across the outer surface quickly enough to supply all the body cells ***[1 mark]***.

Chapter B5

2 a) X = (3 × 3) × 6 = **54 cm^2** ***[1 mark]***
Y = 3 × 3 × 3 = **27 cm^3** ***[1 mark]***
Z = 150 ÷ 125 = **1.2** ***[1 mark]***
b) 5 × 5 × 5, because it has the smallest surface area to volume ratio ***[1 mark]***.

As this cube had the smallest surface area in relation to its volume, it would take the acid longest to diffuse throughout this cube and change its colour.

Page 68 — Human Exchange Surfaces

1 a) C ***[1 mark]***
b) Out of the blood ***[1 mark]***.

2 Any two from: e.g. the small intestine is covered in villi ***[1 mark]***. This increases the surface area for absorption ***[1 mark]***. / The small intestine has a good blood supply ***[1 mark]***. This allows absorption to happen quickly ***[1 mark]***. / The villi have a single layer of surface cells ***[1 mark]***. This means that substances only have a short distance to diffuse across, so absorption can happen quickly ***[1 mark]***. / The cells of the villi have partially permeable membranes ***[1 mark]***. These regulate the movement of substances across them ***[1 mark]***.

3 The breakdown of the walls of the alveoli means that the surface area in the lungs is reduced ***[1 mark]***. This reduces the amount of gas exchange that can take place in the lungs ***[1 mark]*** and therefore the amount of oxygen that can diffuse into the blood ***[1 mark]***.

Pages 69-70 — The Circulatory System

Warm-up

	vena cava	pulmonary vein	pulmonary artery	aorta
oxygenated		✓		✓
deoxygenated	✓		✓	

1 a) X = aorta ***[1 mark]***
Y = pulmonary vein ***[1 mark]***
Z = (right) ventricle ***[1 mark]***
b) 3, 5, 2, 4, 1 ***[2 marks for all correct, 1 mark if all but one are in sequence.]***

2 a) The wall of the left ventricle is thicker than the wall of the right ventricle ***[1 mark]***. This is because the left ventricle needs to generate greater pressure than the right ventricle ***[1 mark]*** because it pumps blood around the whole body, whereas the right ventricle only pumps blood to the lungs ***[1 mark]***.
b) When the ventricles contract, the valves to the atria close and the valves to the blood vessels open ***[1 mark]***. This prevents backflow/the blood from flowing backwards and makes sure that blood flows in the right direction (out of the heart) ***[1 mark]***.

3 a) Mitochondria provide the muscle cells with ATP ***[1 mark]*** which transfers the energy needed for the cardiac muscle to contract and pump blood around the body ***[1 mark]***.
b) i) coronary arteries ***[1 mark]***
ii) E.g. if one of these arteries became blocked, less glucose and oxygen would be able to reach the cells of the heart ***[1 mark]*** and they would die ***[1 mark]***.

Page 71 — Blood Vessels

1 a) i) A ***[1 mark]***
ii) Arteries carry blood under high pressure (unlike veins or capillaries) ***[1 mark]***. This means they need thick muscular walls for strength ***[1 mark]*** and the walls of blood vessel A are the thickest compared to its lumen ***[1 mark]***.
b) i) veins ***[1 mark]***
ii) Blood in veins is at a low pressure ***[1 mark]*** so the valves help to keep the blood flowing in the right direction/prevent backflow ***[1 mark]***.
c) Capillaries carry blood close to cells to exchange substances with them ***[1 mark]***. Having walls that are only one cell thick increases the rate at which substances can diffuse across them ***[1 mark]***, by decreasing the distance over which diffusion occurs ***[1 mark]***.

Page 72 — Blood

1 a) plasma ***[1 mark]***
b) Any three from: e.g. carbon dioxide / urea / hormones / water / glucose / amino acids / antibodies ***[1 mark for each correct answer. Maximum of 3 marks.]***

2 a) They have a biconcave disc shape to give a large surface area for absorbing and releasing oxygen ***[1 mark]***. They don't have a nucleus, which allows more room to carry oxygen ***[1 mark]***. They are small and very flexible which allows them to pass easily through the capillaries ***[1 mark]***.
b) Haemoglobin carries oxygen to body tissues ***[1 mark]***. If there is less haemoglobin in the red blood cells, then the blood will be less able to carry oxygen ***[1 mark]***. This means that the body tissues will receive less oxygen, reducing the amount of aerobic respiration that can take place ***[1 mark]***. This means that less energy is transferred by respiration, causing tiredness ***[1 mark]***.

Page 73 — The Nervous System

1 receptors ***[1 mark]***, sensory ***[1 mark]***, motor ***[1 mark]***, effectors ***[1 mark]***

2 a) i)

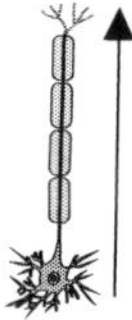

[1 mark]

ii) Part X is the fatty/myelin sheath ***[1 mark]***. It speeds up the electrical/nervous impulse along the neurone ***[1 mark]***.
b) The motor neurones don't work properly, so impulses don't get passed on from the CNS ***[1 mark]*** to the muscles involved in swallowing ***[1 mark]***.

3 By preventing the release of transmitter chemicals, opioids prevent information being transmitted across synapses ***[1 mark]*** between sensory neurones and (relay) neurones in the spinal cord ***[1 mark]***. This means the information about the stimulus doesn't reach the brain, so no pain is felt ***[1 mark]***.

Page 74 — Reflexes

1 Reflex reactions are rapid and involuntary ***[1 mark]***

2 a) i) Y — sensory neurone ***[1 mark]***
Z — relay neurone ***[1 mark]***
ii) synapse ***[1 mark]***
b) the stimulus — flame/heat ***[1 mark]***
the effector — muscle (in arm) ***[1 mark]***
c) The conscious brain isn't involved in a reflex arc ***[1 mark]***.

Page 75 — Hormones and Negative Feedback

1 a) Hormones are released from the endocrine glands directly into the blood ***[1 mark]***. The blood then carries them to other parts of the body ***[1 mark]***. The hormones then bind to receptors on particular effectors and a response is triggered ***[1 mark]***.
b) E.g. a hormonal response is slower than a nervous response ***[1 mark]***. The effects of a hormonal response are longer lasting than the effects of a nervous response ***[1 mark]***.

Chapter B6

c) When the level of a hormone in the blood is above or below the normal level, a response is triggered by negative feedback to bring the level back to normal again ***[1 mark]***.

2 a) E.g. it regulates metabolic rate ***[1 mark]***.

b) When the level of thyroxine in the blood is higher than normal, the secretion of TSH from the pituitary gland is inhibited ***[1 mark]***. This means that the thyroid gland is not stimulated to produce thyroxine ***[1 mark]***, and so the blood thyroxine level falls ***[1 mark]***.

c) E.g. a stressful situation ***[1 mark]***. Adrenaline prepares the body for 'fight or flight' ***[1 mark]*** by activating processes that increase the supply of oxygen and glucose to cells, e.g. it raises heart rate ***[1 mark]***.

Page 76 — Hormones in Reproduction

1 a) A ***[1 mark]***

Oestrogen and progesterone are involved in the growth and maintenance of the uterus lining, so menstruation (the breakdown of the uterus lining) occurs during time period A when the levels of these two hormones are low.

b) oestrogen ***[1 mark]***, progesterone ***[1 mark]***

c) i) It causes an egg to mature in one of the ovaries ***[1 mark]*** and stimulates the ovaries to produce hormones/oestrogen ***[1 mark]***.

ii) After ovulation, the remains of the follicle develop into a corpus luteum ***[1 mark]***, which secretes progesterone ***[1 mark]***. Progesterone inhibits the release of FSH ***[1 mark]*** along with oestrogen ***[1 mark]***.

Page 77 — Hormones for Fertility and Contraception

1 a) Having low FSH levels can mean that eggs don't mature ***[1 mark]***, so ovulation doesn't take place ***[1 mark]***.

b) LH/luteinising hormone ***[1 mark]***

2 a) oestrogen ***[1 mark]***

b) i) Progesterone in the pill inhibits the production of FSH and LH ***[1 mark]***, which stimulate egg maturation and ovulation ***[1 mark]***.

ii) E.g. it stimulates the production of thick cervical mucus, making it less likely that any sperm will get through and reach an egg ***[1 mark]***. / It thins the lining of the uterus, which reduces the chance of a fertilised egg implanting ***[1 mark]***.

c) E.g. she doesn't need to remember to take a pill (at the same time) every day ***[1 mark]***.

Page 78 — More on Contraception

Warm-up

Circled: male condom, female condom, sterilisation, diaphragm, intrauterine devices, 'natural' methods

1 a) female condom/diaphragm ***[1 mark]***

b) They stop the egg and sperm meeting ***[1 mark]***.

c) E.g. hormonal methods are generally more effective at preventing pregnancy than barrier methods when used correctly ***[1 mark]***. Hormonal methods mean the couple don't have to think about contraception each time they have intercourse, unlike with barrier methods ***[1 mark]***.

d) E.g. some barrier methods (such as condoms) can also help to prevent the transmission of STIs ***[1 mark]***. It is less likely that there will be unpleasant side effects as a result of using barrier methods than using hormonal methods ***[1 mark]***.

Pages 79-80 — Homeostasis and Blood Sugar Level

1 allowing large fluctuations in internal conditions ***[1 mark]***

2 a) i) insulin ***[1 mark]***

ii) glucagon ***[1 mark]***

b) It is stored as glycogen in the liver and in the muscles. / It is stored as lipid (fat) in the tissues ***[1 mark]***.

3 a) Conditions in the body need to be kept within a narrow range ***[1 mark]***. If homeostatic mechanisms are faulty, internal conditions may change to fall outside of this range / vary too much from normal levels ***[1 mark]***. This could adversely affect the rate of enzyme-controlled reactions in the body cells / prevent cells from functioning normally ***[1 mark]***.

b) They are needed to detect internal stimuli / changes in the internal conditions of the body ***[1 mark]***.

c) This means that the effectors work in opposition to each other ***[1 mark]***.

4 a) The blood glucose concentration starts increasing as glucose from the drink is absorbed into the blood ***[1 mark]***. The pancreas detects a high blood glucose concentration and secretes insulin ***[1 mark]***. Insulin causes the blood glucose concentration to fall back down ***[1 mark]***.

b) glucagon ***[1 mark]***

c) It increases the concentration of glucose in the blood ***[1 mark]***.

d) Glucagon causes glycogen to be converted into glucose and be released into the blood ***[1 mark]***.

e) E.g. after drinking the glucose drink, the blood glucose concentration would carry on increasing/stay high/not start to fall/fall more slowly ***[1 mark]***.

Page 81 — Diabetes

1 a) E.g. a person's blood glucose level can rise to a level that can kill them / a dangerous level ***[1 mark]***.

b) A person becomes resistant to insulin/their body cells no longer respond to the insulin ***[1 mark]***. / A person doesn't produce enough insulin ***[1 mark]***.

c) Any two from: eating a healthy diet that includes complex carbohydrates ***[1 mark]*** / getting regular exercise ***[1 mark]*** / losing weight (if necessary) ***[1 mark]***.

d) being overweight / obesity ***[1 mark]***

2 a) i) The pancreas of a person with type 1 diabetes doesn't produce insulin ***[1 mark]***, so a pancreas transplant would provide the person with a permanent new source of insulin ***[1 mark]***.

ii) E.g. a pancreas transplant is a serious operation, which carries the risk of complications ***[1 mark]***. / There aren't enough donor pancreases available ***[1 mark]***. / Drugs need to be taken afterwards to suppress the immune system ***[1 mark]***.

You're not expected to know the answer to this question, you're just expected to make a sensible suggestion.

b) E.g. regular insulin injections/insulin therapy ***[1 mark]***.

Chapter B6 — Life on Earth — Past, Present and Future

Pages 82-83 — Natural Selection and Evolution

1 a) Most genetic variants have very little or no effect on the phenotype of an organism ***[1 mark]***.

b) It describes how beneficial genetic variants become more common in a population ***[1 mark]***.

c) By mutations in DNA ***[1 mark]***.

2 a) E.g. organisms have to compete for resources in order to survive ***[1 mark]***, so not all organisms will survive to reproduce and pass their genes on to the next generation ***[1 mark]***.

b) Natural selection means that organisms with the most beneficial genetic variants/alleles ***[1 mark]*** are more likely to pass on their genes to the next generation ***[1 mark]***. Over time this may lead to the most beneficial genetic variants/alleles accumulating in a population and therefore a reduction in the level of genetic variation ***[1 mark]***.

Chapter B6

3 a) E.g. they could allow the two species of wasp to breed with each other and if they are unable to produce fertile offspring the species are separate ***[1 mark]***.

b) A single population of species A became split into two isolated populations when the islands became separated ***[1 mark]***. The environmental conditions on each island were different ***[1 mark]*** and led to natural selection for different genetic variants/alleles in both populations ***[1 mark]***. Over time, the different genetic variants/alleles accumulated in both populations until the two populations were so different they were different species ***[1 mark]***.

4 How to grade your answer:

Level 0: There is no relevant information. ***[0 marks]***

Level 1: There is some information about evolution by natural selection. The points made are basic and not linked together. ***[1-2 marks]***

Level 2: There is some explanation about how evolution by natural selection may lead to a change in the beak size of the finches. Some of the points made are linked together. ***[3-4 marks]***

Level 3: There is a clear and detailed explanation of how evolution by natural selection may lead to a change in the beak size of the finches. The points made are well-linked and the answer has a clear and logical structure. ***[5-6 marks]***

Here are some points your answer may include:

After the storm, there will be fewer larger seeds available on the island.

Birds with larger beaks will be less able to get food.

Small seeds will still be available, so birds with smaller beaks will be better adapted to their environment than the birds with larger beaks.

This makes birds with smaller beaks more likely to survive and reproduce than birds with larger beaks.

In turn, this means that the genetic variants/alleles responsible for small beaks are more likely to be passed on to the next generation than the genetic variants/alleles for larger beaks.

The genetic variants/alleles for smaller beaks will become more common in the population over time and, eventually, all the finches in the population will have smaller beaks.

Page 84 — Evidence for Evolution

1 a) The remains of an insect which died recently ***[1 mark]***.

b) Fossil B, Fossil A, Human foot ***[1 mark]***

You know that the fossils are form the ancestors of humans, so the human foot must be the most recent. Fossil A more closely resembles the human foot than fossil B, so it must be the next most recent.

2 a) The fast reproduction rate means the scientists can study evolution as it is happening ***[1 mark]***.

b) By mutations in the bacterial DNA ***[1 mark]***.

c) The findings suggest that bacterial cells with the ability to use citrate as food source are more likely to survive once the glucose supply has run out ***[1 mark]***. These bacterial cells are therefore more likely to reproduce and pass on their genes to the next generation ***[1 mark]***, meaning that the ability to use citrate has become more common in the population ***[1 mark]***.

Page 85 — Selective Breeding

Warm-up

Producing bacteria with the human gene for insulin. Creating hens that lay eggs containing human proteins. Creating a crop plant that secretes scorpion venom.

Selective breeding is used to create different varieties of the same species. It can't be used to introduce genetic material from another organism, such as a gene from a human into a bacterium — for this you would need to use genetic engineering techniques.

1 Darwin noticed that selective breeding produced new varieties of organisms which were sometimes very different to their wild ancestors ***[1 mark]***. This led him to think that natural processes selected individuals with traits which made them more likely to survive in an environment ***[1 mark]***, meaning that these traits became more common and the species evolved ***[1 mark]***.

2 a) Select only those hens with a high egg production for further breeding with males ***[1 mark]***. Select the offspring with the highest egg production and breed them with males ***[1 mark]***. Continue to breed the most desirable offspring over several generations, so that the egg production gets higher and higher ***[1 mark]***.

b) The selective breeding of the cows has reduced the gene pool for his herd ***[1 mark]***. A smaller gene pool means that it's more likely that individuals will inherit harmful genetic defects, such as Weaver Syndrome ***[1 mark]***.

Page 86 — Classification

1 a) The grouping of living organisms ***[1 mark]*** based on similarities and differences between them ***[1 mark]***.

b) i) B ***[1 mark]***

ii) G and H ***[1 mark]***

2 a) Organism F ***[1 mark]*** as its DNA has the highest percentage similarity (96%) to human DNA of the organisms in the table ***[1 mark]***.

b) Scientists can find the number of genetic variants between two species ***[1 mark]*** and use an estimate for the frequency at which mutations happen in each species ***[1 mark]*** to estimate how long ago speciation occurred ***[1 mark]***.

Pages 87-88 — Biodiversity

Warm-up

greater, more, damage, decrease

1 a) The rate at which resources are used is not greater than the rate at which they can be replaced ***[1 mark]***.

b) living organisms ***[1 mark]***, genes and alleles ***[1 mark]***

2 a) Human activities are having such a rapid effect that there is not enough time for populations to adapt to the changes ***[1 mark]***.

b) E.g. the loss of one species can impact on food chains ***[1 mark]***, and may lead to the loss of other species ***[1 mark]***.

3 a) E.g. increasing industrialisation is leading to an increased use of raw materials ***[1 mark]***. This has led to increased habitat destruction in the extraction of raw materials ***[1 mark]***. Increasing industrialisation has also led to the increased production of waste from industrial processes ***[1 mark]***. This can result in increased pollution of ecosystems ***[1 mark]***.

b) E.g. large companies may sell the 'best' variety of a particular natural resource (such as seeds), resulting in it being used across the world ***[1 mark]***, reducing the number of varieties used globally, and reducing global biodiversity ***[1 mark]***.

4 How to grade your answer:

Level 0: There is no relevant information. ***[0 marks]***

Level 1: There is some discussion of how humans can help to protect biodiversity on several different levels. The points made are basic and not linked together. ***[1-2 marks]***

Level 2: There is some discussion of how humans can help to protect biodiversity on a species, habitat and global level. Some of the points made are linked together. ***[3-4 marks]***

Level 3: There is a clear and detailed discussion of how humans can help to protect biodiversity on a species, habitat and global level. The points made are well-linked and the answer has a clear and logical structure. ***[5-6 marks]***

Chapter C1

Here are some points your answer may include:
Humans can protect individual species by banning the hunting of the species, or by keeping individuals of the species in safe areas away from hunting or habitat destruction.
Safe areas for animals include zoos and for plants they include botanical gardens and seed banks.
Humans can protect habitats and ecosystems by creating protected areas such as national parks and nature reserves in which development of land is restricted.
They can also create protected areas in the sea to protect marine ecosystems from human activities such as fishing.
Humans could help to protect biodiversity on a global scale by reducing the amount of greenhouse gases released by human activities.
This would help to reduce global warming.
Global warming may lead to the extinction of species, so preventing it from happening would help to protect global biodiversity.

Page 89 — Maintaining Biodiversity

1 a) If one species goes extinct then the food chain that it is a part of will be disrupted ***[1 mark]***. Protecting one species,will help to protect the species that feed on it ***[1 mark]***. / Efforts to protect one species may involve the protection of the habitat of that species ***[1 mark]***, in which case, other species within that habitat will also be protected ***[1 mark]***.

b) E.g. the costs involved in conserving the species may outweigh the potential benefit ***[1 mark]***.

2 a) E.g. regions of high biodiversity may have plants which contain undiscovered medicines which could be used by humans ***[1 mark]***. / Protecting regions of high biodiversity may help to protect species which are used by humans for industrial materials and fuels ***[1 mark]***. / Protecting regions of high biodiversity may help to protect the human food supply ***[1 mark]***.

b) E.g. protected areas prevent people from being able to use the land for human activities such as building/farming ***[1 mark]*** or for using/selling the natural resources it has ***[1 mark]***. Some people think this is morally wrong in developing countries because these activities could help to boost their economy ***[1 mark]***.

c) E.g. it may be difficult to get two or more countries to work together to establish parks like La Amistad International Park ***[1 mark]***, because they may not be willing to sign up to an agreement not to develop the land ***[1 mark]***.

Chapter C1 — Air and Water

Page 90 — States of Matter

Warm-up
Particles in liquids are held in fixed positions by strong forces.

1 When a physical change occurs, there are no new substances made ***[1 mark]***. During a chemical change, the atoms rearrange themselves to form new products ***[1 mark]***.

2 a) Any two from e.g.: Particles are not solid spheres, they are atoms, ions, or molecules. / The model doesn't show the size of the particle. / The model doesn't show the space between particles. / The model doesn't show forces between particles, so their strength is unknown.
[2 marks — 1 mark for each correct answer]

b) Particles in liquids are constantly moving with a random motion ***[1 mark]***, whereas particles in solids vibrate around fixed positions ***[1 mark]***.

Page 91 — Changing State

1 a) melting ***[1 mark]***

b) boiling point ***[1 mark]***

c) The bonds are strong ***[1 mark]***.

2 a) sodium chloride ***[1 mark]***

At 900 °C, water would be a gas and copper would be a solid.

b) Sodium chloride ***[1 mark]*** and water ***[1 mark]***.

At 1500 °C, copper would be a liquid.

c) Boiling sodium chloride ***[1 mark]***.

d) Yes. Copper boils at a higher temperature than water ***[1 mark]***, so more energy is needed to break the bonds between the copper atoms than between the water molecules ***[1 mark]***.

Page 92 — Chemical Formulas

Warm-up
B, Sn, Mn, Cl

1 a) Sulfur, hydrogen and oxygen ***[2 marks for all three correct, otherwise 1 mark for two correct]***

b) $H_2S_2O_6$ ***[1 mark]***

2 a) water ***[1 mark]***

b) 6 ***[1 mark]***

C_2H_4 contains 2 carbon atoms and 4 hydrogen atoms.

c) D ***[1 mark]***

d) The formula of a molecular compound tells you how many atoms there are in a molecule ***[1 mark]***, whereas the formula of an ionic compound tells you the ratio of the elements in a compound ***[1 mark]***.

Pages 93-94 — Chemical Equations

For all the equations in the answers below (and any other 'balanced equation' questions), you'll get the marks if your equation is equivalent to the answer given — in other words, if you've got the same equation, but with all the numbers of moles multiplied by the same number.

Warm-up
1) — True, 2) — False, 3) — True, 4) — True

1 a) potassium + chlorine → potassium chloride ***[1 mark]***

b) $2K + Cl_2 \rightarrow 2KCl$ ***[1 mark]***

2 methane + steam → carbon monoxide + hydrogen ***[1 mark]***

3 $4Na + O_2 \rightarrow 2Na_2O$
[2 marks for all formulas correct and a correctly-balanced equation, otherwise 1 mark for correct formulas in an unbalanced equation.]

4 a) $\mathbf{4}NH_3 + \mathbf{5}O_2 \rightarrow \mathbf{4}NO + \mathbf{6}H_2O$ ***[1 mark]***

b) E.g. there are 7 oxygen atoms on the left-hand side of the equation and only 6 on the right-hand side ***[1 mark]***.

5 $\mathbf{2}Al_{(s)} + \mathbf{3}H_2SO_{4\,(aq)} \rightarrow Al_2(SO_4)_{3\,(aq)} + \mathbf{3}H_{2\,(g)}$
[2 marks for correct answer, otherwise 1 mark for some correct working.]

6 $S + \mathbf{6}HNO_3 \rightarrow H_2SO_4 + \mathbf{6}NO_2 + \mathbf{2}H_2O$
[2 marks for correct answer, otherwise 1 mark for some correct working.]

Page 95 — Endothermic and Exothermic Reactions

1 B ***[1 mark]***

2

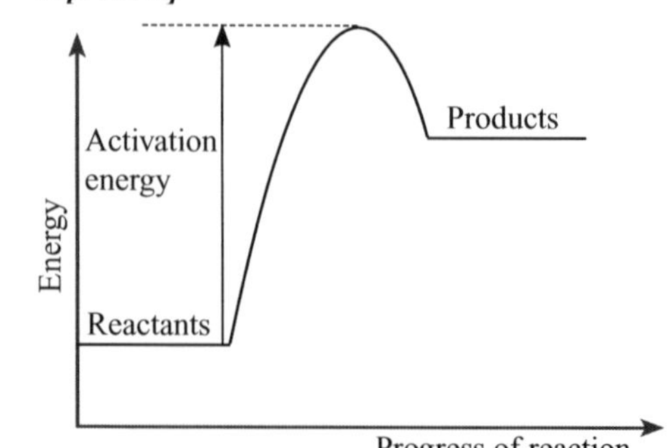

Chapter C1

[1 mark for reactants and products correctly labelled and at appropriate energies, 1 mark for correct shape of curve, 1 mark for activation energy correctly labelled.]

3 Reaction A is the most suitable reaction *[1 mark]*.
Reaction C is endothermic, so would not give out heat, and couldn't be used to warm your hands *[1 mark]*.
Reaction A has a lower activation energy than Reaction B / gives out more energy than Reaction B *[1 mark]*.

Pages 96-97 — Bond Energies

Warm-up

During exothermic reactions, the energy taken to break the bonds in the reactants is less than the energy released by making the bonds in the products.

1 a) energy change = energy required to break bonds – energy released by forming bonds
bonds broken: 1 × C=C + 1 × H—O
= 614 + 463 = 1077 kJ/mol *[1 mark]*
bonds made: 1 × C—C + 1 × C—H + 1 × C—O
= 347 + 413 + 358 = 1118 kJ/mol *[1 mark]*
energy change = 1077 – 1118 = **–41 kJ/mol** *[1 mark]*

If there are any bonds that appear on both sides of the equation, you can ignore them when you work out the energies of the bonds broken and the bonds made — that's what we've done here. But if you find it easier to work out the total energy of all the bonds in the products and the total energy of all the bonds in the reactants, you'll still get the same answer.

b) The reaction is exothermic *[1 mark]* as the energy change of reaction is negative / energy is given out during the reaction / it takes less energy to break the bonds in the reactants than the energy given out when the bonds in the products are made *[1 mark]*.

If you calculated a positive energy change in part a), you would still get the marks for part b) if you correctly explain why a reaction with a positive energy change is endothermic.

2 a) exothermic *[1 mark]*

b) energy change = energy required to break bonds – energy released by forming bonds
bonds broken: 1 × C—H + 1 × Cl—Cl
= 413 + 239 = 652 kJ/mol
bonds made: 1 × C—Cl + 1 × H—Cl = 339 + H—Cl
–119 = 652 – (339 + H—Cl)
–119 = 313 – H—Cl
H—Cl = 313 + 119 = **432 kJ/mol**
[3 marks for the correct answer, otherwise 1 mark for correct expression for the value of the H—Cl bond in terms of the energy change of reaction and the energies of the bonds made and broken, 1 mark for correctly calculating energies of bonds made and broken]

c) Cl—Cl, C—Cl, C—C, C—H, H—Cl
[1 mark for correct order, using value for H—Cl calculated in part b).]

Stronger bonds take more energy to break, so stronger bonds will have higher bond energies.

Page 98 — The Evolution of the Atmosphere

1 The gases that made up Earth's early atmosphere were released by volcanic eruptions *[1 mark]*.

2 a) i) carbon dioxide *[1 mark]*

ii) Any two from, e.g: cyanobacteria/plants evolved which removed carbon dioxide through photosynthesis / carbon dioxide was locked in fossil fuels/sedimentary rocks / carbon dioxide dissolved in the oceans *[1 mark for each correct answer]*.

b) As cyanobacteria/green plants photosynthesised, they produced oxygen *[1 mark]*. Hardly any oxygen is present in Mars' atmosphere as there are no cyanobacteria/plants / there is no discovered life on Mars *[1 mark]*.

c) nitrogen *[1 mark]*

Page 99 — Combustion and Air Pollution

1 a) oxidation *[1 mark]*

b) Where there isn't enough oxygen for complete combustion *[1 mark]*.

c) i) e.g. fainting / comas / death *[1 mark]*

ii) e.g. respiratory problems *[1 mark]*

2 a) City A, as there are high levels of particulate carbon here *[1 mark]*. Particulate carbon, once it's escaped into the atmosphere, will eventually fall back to the ground as a black deposit which can coat buildings *[1 mark]*.

b) City B, as it has the highest levels of nitrogen dioxide and sulfur dioxide *[1 mark]*. These pollutants mix with clouds and form dilute nitric and sulfuric acids, which fall as acid rain and can damage buildings *[1 mark]*.

c) Any two from, e.g.: using fuels that don't contain sulfur / using acid gas scrubbers in power stations / using catalytic converters *[2 marks — 1 mark for each correct answer]*

Pages 100-101 — Greenhouse Gases and Climate Change

1 a) Nitrogen *[1 mark]*

b) They help to keep Earth warm *[1 mark]*.

2 a) E.g. an atmospheric gas that absorbs and reflects thermal radiation *[1 mark]*.

b) E.g. Elvis is incorrect. The greenhouse effect is important as it keeps the Earth warm enough to support life *[1 mark]*.

c) Any two from: e.g. severe flooding / changing rainfall patterns / melting polar ice caps *[1 mark for each correct answer]*.

d) E.g. Earth's climate has lots of variables so it's hard to model / we don't know how greenhouse gas emissions might change in the future *[1 mark]*.

3 How to grade your answer:

Level 0: There is no relevant information *[No marks]*.

Level 1: Unstructured and no logic. The trends in the variables are described but reasons are not given *[1 to 2 marks]*.

Level 2: Some structure and logic but lacking clarity. The trends in the variables are described and there is some explanation of how the increase in carbon dioxide may have come about and how this might be linked to temperature *[3 to 4 marks]*.

Level 3: Clear, logical answer. The trends in the variables are described and there is a clear explanation of how the increase in carbon dioxide may have come about and how this may be linked to temperature *[5 to 6 marks]*.

Here are some points your answer may include:
The graph shows an increase in carbon dioxide levels in the atmosphere over the time period covered by the graph.
The increase in carbon dioxide levels is likely to be largely due to human activities which release carbon dioxide into the atmosphere.
These activities include increased burning of fossil fuels, increased deforestation and increased waste production.
The graph shows that the increase in carbon dioxide appears to correlate with an increase in global temperatures.
The increase in global temperatures is likely to be due to the increase in carbon dioxide in the atmosphere, as carbon dioxide is a greenhouse gas so helps to keep Earth warm.

Chapter C2

4 E.g. the conclusion is not valid. The CO_2 emissions from burning fossil fuels are only from one country and are not a global figure ***[1 mark]***. The global CO_2 emissions from burning fossil fuels may be increasing so there could be a link between CO_2 emissions and a rise in sea levels ***[1 mark]***. The data also only shows CO_2 emissions from burning fossil fuels ***[1 mark]***. CO_2 emissions from all sources should be considered for the conclusion to be valid ***[1 mark]***.

Page 102 — Reducing Pollution

1 a) When enough CO_2 is removed from the atmosphere to cancel out the greenhouse gases emitted ***[1 mark]***.

b) Any two from: e.g. by buying carbon credits / by planting trees / by capturing gases that are released ***[2 marks — 1 mark for each correct answer]***.

c) E.g. governments might be reluctant to impose these methods if they think it will affect economic growth / could impact on people's well-being ***[1 mark]*** especially if other countries aren't using these methods either / the country is still developing ***[1 mark]***.

2 a) E.g. carbon dioxide produced by burning fossil fuels and by other means is captured before it's released into the atmosphere ***[1 mark]*** and then stored deep underground ***[1 mark]***.

b) E.g. carbon capture takes lots of energy, so could reduce the efficiency of a power station ***[1 mark]***.

c) E.g. the scale of greenhouse gas emissions is so large that carbon capture schemes alone couldn't reduce them entirely ***[1 mark]***.

Page 103 — Tests for Gases

1 a) damp blue litmus paper ***[1 mark]***

b) chlorine ***[1 mark]***

2 a) E.g. the gas could be toxic/an irritant ***[1 mark]***

b) Bubble the gas through limewater ***[1 mark]***. If the gas is carbon dioxide, the limewater will turn cloudy ***[1 mark]***.

c) The gas was not hydrogen ***[1 mark]***.

d) oxygen ***[1 mark]***

Page 104 — Potable Water

1 pure water ***[1 mark]***

2 a) filtration ***[1 mark]***

b) Chlorine gas is bubbled through the water to kill harmful bacteria / microbes ***[1 mark]***.

3 a) Kuwait distils seawater as a source of drinking water as it has a low annual rainfall ***[1 mark]***, so groundwater and surface water are unlikely to be readily available / seawater is likely to be the most accessible water ***[1 mark]***.

b) Any one from: e.g. it requires lots of energy / it's expensive / it's impractical ***[1 mark]***.

c) E.g. using membranes / reverse osmosis ***[1 mark]***

Chapter C2 — Chemical Patterns

Page 105 — The History of the Atom

Warm-up

Plum pudding model — A positively charged 'ball' with negatively charged electrons in it.

Ancient Greek model — Everything is made up of four elements — earth, air, fire and water.

Rutherford's nuclear model — A small, positively charged nucleus surrounded by a 'cloud' of negative electrons.

1 Tiny solid spheres that can't be divided ***[1 mark]***.

2 a) Atoms are neutral / have no overall charge ***[1 mark]***. Therefore there must have been positive charge to balance the negative charge of the electrons ***[1 mark]***.

b) During the gold foil experiment, most of the particles did pass straight through the foil ***[1 mark]*** as most of the atom is 'empty' space ***[1 mark]***. However, a small number of particles were deflected more than expected, and some were even deflected backwards ***[1 mark]*** because they came near the concentrated, positive charge of the nucleus ***[1 mark]***.

Page 106 — The Atom

1 a) neutron: 0 charge ***[1 mark]***
proton: +1 charge ***[1 mark]***

b) –1 ***[1 mark]***

c) one hundred-thousandth of the atomic diameter ***[1 mark]***

2 a) The length of a chemical bond ***[1 mark]***.

b) Electrons move around the nucleus in electron shells/orbitals ***[1 mark]***. The volume of these shells determines the size of the atom ***[1 mark]***.

Page 107 — Atoms, Ions and Isotopes

1 a) The atom gains one or more electrons ***[1 mark]***.

b) Number of electrons = 12 – 2 = **10** ***[1 mark]***

An ion with a 2+ charge has lost two electrons.

2 a)

Isotope	No. of Protons	No. of Neutrons	No. of Electrons
^{32}S	**16**	**16**	16
^{33}S	**16**	**17**	**16**
^{34}S	**16**	**18**	**16**
^{36}S	**16**	**20**	**16**

[3 marks for all rows correct, otherwise 2 marks for 3 rows correct, and 1 mark for 1 or 2 rows correct.]

b) X and Z are isotopes ***[1 mark]***. They have the same atomic number / same number of protons ***[1 mark]*** but different mass numbers / numbers of neutrons ***[1 mark]***.

Page 108 — The Periodic Table

1 a) By atomic number ***[1 mark]***.

b) Elements in Period 4 have one more shell of electrons than elements in Period 3 that are in the same group ***[1 mark]***.

2 a) It allowed him to keep elements with similar properties in the same group ***[1 mark]***.

b) $EkCl_4$ ***[1 mark]***

c) The properties of these newly discovered elements matched Mendeleev's predictions for the properties of the elements that would fill the gaps in the table ***[1 mark]***.

Page 109 — Electronic Structure

1 8 ***[1 mark]***

The electronic structure of neon is 2.8, which means there are 8 electrons in its outer shell.

2 a) 2.8.6 ***[1 mark]***

b)

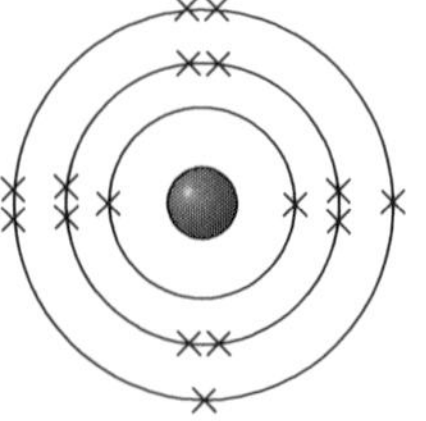

[1 mark]

3 a) Be ***[1 mark]***

b) The group number tells you how many electrons are in the outer shell, so magnesium has 2 outer shell electrons ***[1 mark]***. The period number tells you how many electron shells the atom has in total, so magnesium has three shells ***[1 mark]***. All the shells apart from the outer shell will be filled (the first holds 2 electrons and the second holds 8) ***[1 mark]***. So the electronic structure of magnesium must be 2.8.2 ***[1 mark]***.

Chapter C2

Page 110 — Metals and Non-Metals

1 a) E.g. metals: towards the left.
non-metals: towards the right ***[1 mark]***.

b) Elements that react to form positive ions are metals ***[1 mark]***.

c) ionic bonds ***[1 mark]***
metallic bonds ***[1 mark]***

d) Both are metals that lose their (2 or 3) outer shell electrons ***[1 mark]*** to form positive ions ***[1 mark]***.

2 Iron is a typical metal and therefore has a higher density / is good at conducting heat/electricity / has a high boiling/ melting point / is shiny ***[1 mark for each property up to a maximum of 2 marks]***. Sulfur is a non-metal and therefore has a lower density / doesn't conduct heat/electricity / has a lower melting and boiling point / is dull looking ***[1 mark for each property up to a maximum of 2 marks]***.

Pages 111-112 — Group 1 Elements

Warm-up

Statement	True	False
Group 1 elements are non-metals.		✓
Group 1 metals tarnish in moist air.	✓	
Density decreases as you go down Group 1.		✓
Group 1 metals get harder down the group.		✓
Lithium is less dense than water.	✓	
Storing sodium in oil prevents it from tarnishing.	✓	

1 potassium hydroxide ***[1 mark]***
hydrogen ***[1 mark]***

2 a) The Group 1 elements all have one outer electron ***[1 mark]***, so losing one electron gives them a 1+ charge with a stable electronic structure/full outer shell ***[1 mark]***.

b) Any answer in the range 64 °C to 180 °C ***[1 mark]***.

3 a) i) lithium chloride ***[1 mark]***

ii) $2Li_{(s)} + Cl_{2(g)} \rightarrow 2LiCl_{(s)}$ ***[1 mark for correct reactants and products, 1 mark for correctly balancing the equation, 1 mark for correct state symbols.]***

b) The reaction with potassium will also produce a metal chloride — potassium chloride ***[1 mark]***. They react in a similar way because lithium and potassium both have a single outer electron ***[1 mark]***.

c) The reaction is slower so metal **A** must be less reactive than sodium ***[1 mark]***. Reactivity increases as you go down Group 1 ***[1 mark]*** so metal **A** must be lithium which is higher up Group 1/less reactive than sodium ***[1 mark]***.

4 a) Francium would be more reactive than caesium ***[1 mark]***. As you go further down the group the outer electron is further away from the nucleus ***[1 mark]***, so the attraction between the nucleus and the electron decreases and the electron is more easily lost ***[1 mark]***.

b) Formula: Fr_3P ***[1 mark]***
Equation: $12Fr + P_4 \rightarrow 4Fr_3P$ ***[1 mark for correct reactants and products, 1 mark for correctly balancing the equation.]***

Pages 113-114 — Group 7 Elements

1 Halogens are non-metals that exist as molecules of two atoms ***[1 mark]***.
Chlorine is a green gas at room temperature ***[1 mark]***.

2 a) sodium bromide ***[1 mark]***

b) $2K_{(s)} + F_{2(g)} \rightarrow 2KF_{(s)}$
[1 mark for correct reactants and products, 1 mark for correctly balancing the equation, 1 mark for correct state symbols.]

3 a) Group 7 elements have seven electrons in their outer shell ***[1 mark]***. As you go further down the group additional shells are added / the outer electrons are further away from the nucleus ***[1 mark]***.

b) E.g. both iodine and fluorine have 7 outer shell electrons so react in a similar way ***[1 mark]***. So iodine will react with sodium to form sodium iodide ***[1 mark]***. However, iodine will react more slowly than fluorine ***[1 mark]*** since reactivity decreases down the group ***[1 mark]***.

4 a) chlorine water and sodium iodide solution:
solution turns brown ***[1 mark]***
bromine water and sodium bromide solution:
no reaction ***[1 mark]***

b) Iodine is less reactive than bromine ***[1 mark]***, so iodine cannot displace bromine from sodium bromide ***[1 mark]***.

c) $Cl_2 + 2NaBr \rightarrow Br_2 + 2NaCl$
[1 mark for all reactants and products correct, 1 mark for equation being correctly balanced.]

d) Yes ***[1 mark]***, as chlorine is more reactive than astatine ***[1 mark]***.

Page 115 — Group 0 Elements

1 They are monatomic ***[1 mark]***.

2 Argon has a full outer shell of electrons, giving it a stable electronic structure ***[1 mark]***. It won't easily give up or gain electrons, making it inert ***[1 mark]***. This means that it won't react with the metals/form compounds with the metals ***[1 mark]***.

3 a) A boiling point between –152 °C and 20 °C ***[1 mark]***.

b) A density between 1.0 kg/m^3 and 3.6 kg/m^3 ***[1 mark]***.

Pages 116-118 — Ionic Compounds

Warm-up

Dot and cross diagram	Chemical formula
$[Na]^+$ $[Cl]^-$	**NaCl**
$[Na]^+$ $[O]^{2-}$ $[Na]^+$	**Na_2O**
$[Cl]^-$ $[Mg]^{2+}$ $[Cl]^-$	**$MgCl_2$**

1 calcium chloride ***[1 mark]***
potassium oxide ***[1 mark]***

Compounds that contain ionic bonding have to be made up of a metal and a non-metal. All the other options only contain non-metals, so can't be held together by ionic bonds.

2 a) CaF_2 ***[1 mark]***

b)

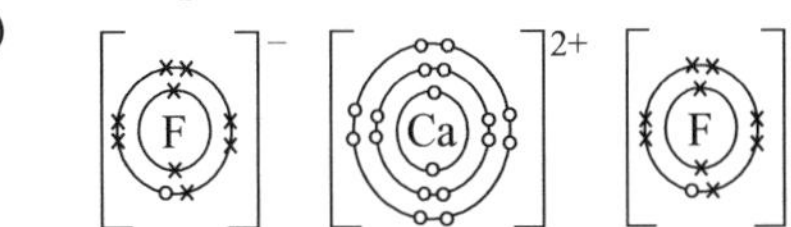

[1 mark for correct electronic structure of fluoride ions, 1 mark for correct electronic structure of calcium ions, 1 mark for correct charges on calcium ion and fluoride ions.]

If you only showed the outer electron shells of the ions, you would also get the mark.

3 a)

Ionic Compound	Cation	Anion	Chemical Formula
Calcium chloride	**Ca^{2+}**	Cl^-	$CaCl_2$
Barium nitrate	Ba^{2+}	NO_3^-	**$Ba(NO_3)_2$**
Potassium carbonate	K^+	CO_3^{2-}	**K_2CO_3**
Lithium oxide	Li^+	**O^{2-}**	Li_2O

[1 mark for each correct answer]

Chapter C3

b) The ions in lithium oxide are held together by strong electrostatic forces of attraction/ionic bonds ***[1 mark]***. A greater amount of energy is needed to overcome these forces compared to the forces in carbon monoxide, so lithium oxide has a higher melting point ***[1 mark]***.

4 a) BeS ***[1 mark]***

b) Beryllium sulfide contains positive beryllium ions (Be^{2+}) ***[1 mark]*** and negative sulfide ions (S^{2-}) ***[1 mark]*** that are arranged in a regular lattice/giant ionic lattice ***[1 mark]***. The oppositely charged ions are held together by electrostatic forces acting in all directions ***[1 mark]***.

5 Boiling point: Potassium bromide has a giant structure with strong ionic bonds ***[1 mark]***. In order to boil, these bonds need to be broken, which takes a lot of energy ***[1 mark]***.
Electrical conductivity of solid: The ions are in fixed positions in the lattice ***[1 mark]*** and so are not able to move and carry a charge through the solid ***[1 mark]***.
Electrical conductivity of solution: In solution, the ions are free to move ***[1 mark]*** and can carry a charge from place to place ***[1 mark]***.
Solubility in water: The charges of the ions allow them to interact with the water molecules ***[1 mark]***.

6 a)

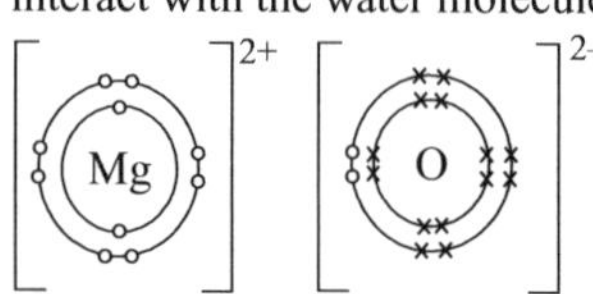

[1 mark for correct electronic structure of magnesium ion, 1 mark for correct electronic structure of oxide ion, 1 mark for correct charges on magnesium ion and oxide ions.]

If you only showed the outer electron shells of the ions, you would also get the marks.

b) MgO ***[1 mark]***

Remember that the overall charge of the ionic compound must be neutral. So you can work out the empirical formula by seeing that you only need one oxide ion to balance the charge on a magnesium ion.

c) How to grade your answer:
Level 0: There is no relevant information ***[No marks]***.
Level 1: The discussion is limited and doesn't mention both the uses and limitations of dot and cross diagrams ***[1 to 2 marks]***.
Level 2: There is some discussion of dot and cross diagrams, with at least one use and one limitation covered ***[3 to 4 marks]***.
Level 3: The discussion is comprehensive in evaluating both the uses and limitations of dot and cross diagrams ***[5 to 6 marks]***.
Here are some points your answer may include:
<u>Dot and cross diagrams show:</u>
Charge of the ions.
The arrangement of electrons in an atom or ion.
Which atoms the electrons in an ion originally come from.
Empirical formula (correct ratio of ions).
<u>Dot and cross diagrams do not:</u>
Show the structure of the compound.
Correctly represent the sizes of ions.

Chapter C3 — Chemicals of the Natural Environment

Page 119 — Metallic Bonding and Reactivity

Warm-up
good conductor of heat, high melting point, malleable, crystal structure when solid

1 The easier it is for a metal atom to form a positive ion, the less reactive it will be ***[1 mark]***.

2 a) Delocalised electrons
Metal ions

[1 mark for showing positive metal ions, 1 mark for showing free electrons, 1 mark for correct labels.]

b) i) Metals usually have high melting points because a large amount of energy is needed to overcome the strong electrostatic attraction ***[1 mark]*** between the positive ions and the delocalised 'sea' of electrons ***[1 mark]***.

ii) The delocalised electrons are free to move ***[1 mark]***, so they can carry a charge through the solid metal ***[1 mark]***.

Page 120 — Ionic Equations and Reactions of Metals

1 $Ag^{+}_{(aq)} + Cl^{-}_{(aq)} \rightarrow AgCl_{(s)}$
[2 marks for all formulas correct and a correctly-balanced equation, otherwise 1 mark for correct formulas in an unbalanced equation.]

2 a) Yes, because lead can displace silver from a salt solution / silver cannot displace lead from a salt solution ***[1 mark]***.

b) $3Mg + 2AlCl_3 \rightarrow 2Al + 3MgCl_2$
[2 marks for all formulas correct and a correctly-balanced equation, otherwise 1 mark for correct formulas in an unbalanced equation.]

c) The solution would change colour from colourless to green ***[1 mark]***. The piece of shiny grey nickel will be coated in dull grey lead ***[1 mark]***.

Pages 121-122 — More Reactions of Metals

1 a) Most reactive: magnesium
zinc
iron
Least reactive: copper
[1 mark for putting magnesium at the top and copper at the bottom. 1 mark for putting zinc above iron in the middle.]

b) i) zinc oxide ***[1 mark]***

ii) Metal X was sodium, because it reacted vigorously with cold water ***[1 mark]***.

2 a) $Mg + 2H^{+} \rightarrow Mg^{2+} + H_2$
[2 marks for all formulas correct and a correctly-balanced equation, otherwise 1 mark for correct formulas in an unbalanced equation.]

b) When a metal reacts with an acid, the metal forms positive ions ***[1 mark]***. The results show that lithium reacts more vigorously with acid than magnesium does ***[1 mark]***, so lithium forms positive ions more easily ***[1 mark]***.

c) A very vigorous fizzing/more vigorous than lithium ***[1 mark]***, sodium disappears ***[1 mark]***.

d) lithium, calcium, copper ***[1 mark]***

e) It is not possible to tell the difference between magnesium and zinc from these results since both have the same reaction with dilute acid ***[1 mark]***. E.g. to find which is more reactive, you could find the effect of adding zinc to water ***[1 mark]***.

Pages 123-124 — Extracting Metals

1 a) Tin can be extracted from its ore by reduction with carbon ***[1 mark]***.

b) Any one from: copper / zinc ***[1 mark]***.

2 Iron is below carbon in the reactivity series so can be extracted by heating its ore with carbon ***[1 mark]***. Aluminium is above carbon so it has to be extracted by electrolysis ***[1 mark]***. Electrolysis is more expensive as it uses more energy ***[1 mark]*** because you need to melt the ore, then pass an electric current through it ***[1 mark]***.

Chapter C3

3 a) Phytoextraction uses plants to extract metals from their ores ***[1 mark]***. Plants are grown on soil containing copper compounds ***[1 mark]***, so as they grow, copper builds up in their leaves ***[1 mark]***. The plants are burned ***[1 mark]***. The resulting ash contains the copper compounds ***[1 mark]***.

b) By electrolysis of a solution containing the copper compounds ***[1 mark]*** or by displacement using scrap iron ***[1 mark]***.

c) Advantage: e.g. less damaging to the environment than traditional methods ***[1 mark]***.
Disadvantage: e.g. process is very slow ***[1 mark]***.

d) E.g. bioleaching / bacterial methods ***[1 mark]***.

4 a) E.g. $ZnO + C \rightarrow Zn + CO$ / $2ZnO + C \rightarrow 2Zn + CO_2$ ***[1 mark for correct equation, 1 mark for correct balancing.]***

b) The impurity is iron as iron is lower than carbon in the reactivity series/less reactive than carbon ***[1 mark]***, so the iron oxide present in the mixture would have been reduced by carbon, as well as the zinc oxide, in the blast furnace ***[1 mark]***.

Calcium is more reactive than carbon so the calcium in calcium oxide wouldn't be reduced to calcium metal in the blast furnace.

Page 125 — Oxidation and Reduction

1 Oxidation can describe the addition of oxygen. During the combustion of a hydrocarbon, the hydrocarbon is burnt in oxygen so oxygen-containing products are made ***[1 mark]***.

2 Reduction is the loss of electrons ***[1 mark]***.

3 a) $Al \rightarrow Al^{3+} + 3e^-$ ***[1 mark]***

b) $2Al + 3Cu^{2+} \rightarrow 2Al^{3+} + 3Cu$ ***[1 mark]***

4 a) i) $Zn \rightarrow Zn^{2+} + 2e^-$ ***[1 mark]***

ii) $2H^+ + 2e^- \rightarrow H_2$ ***[1 mark]***

b) zinc ***[1 mark]***

Pages 126-128 — Electrolysis

Warm-up

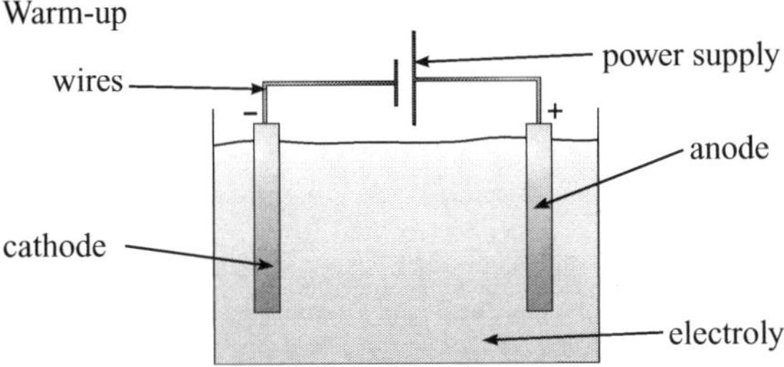

1 a) The ions in solid sodium chloride are not free to move and so can't carry a charge ***[1 mark]***. When sodium chloride is molten or dissolved it can carry a charge as the ions are free to move around ***[1 mark]***.

b) The sodium ions move towards the cathode/negative electrode and the chloride ions move towards the anode/ positive electrode ***[1 mark]***.

2 a) molten aluminium ***[1 mark]***

b) Carbon in the anode reacts with oxygen to form carbon dioxide ***[1 mark]***, so it degrades over time ***[1 mark]***.

3 a) H_2O^- ***[1 mark]***

b) i) Bubbles of gas would form ***[1 mark]***.

ii) Copper metal would coat the electrode ***[1 mark]***.

4 a) PbI_2 ***[1 mark]***

b) Lead metal would form at the cathode ***[1 mark]***.

5 a) Inert electrodes do not react with the electrolyte ***[1 mark]***.

b) Disagree. Potassium nitrate solution will contain hydrogen and hydroxide ions, as well as potassium and nitrate ions ***[1 mark]***. Since potassium is more reactive than hydrogen, hydrogen will be discharged instead ***[1 mark]***.

c) At the anode, you would see bubbles of gas ***[1 mark]*** as oxygen is evolved ***[1 mark]***.

6 a) E.g.

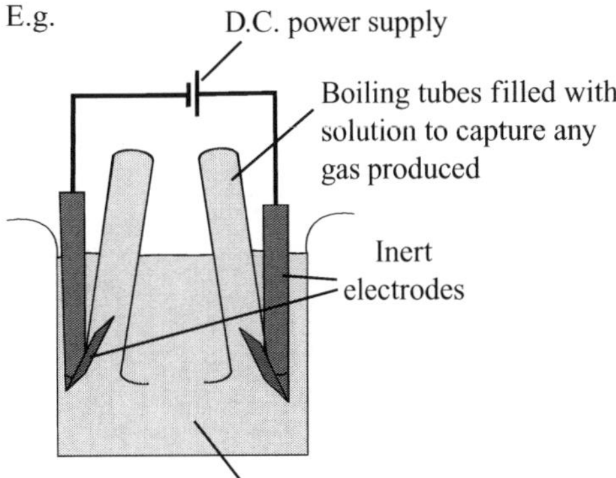

[1 mark for power supply, 1 mark for electrodes in solution, 1 mark for boiling tubes or other similar collector over the electrodes, 1 mark for labels.]

b)

Solution	Product at cathode	Product at anode
$CuCl_2$	Cu	Cl_2
KBr	H_2	Br_2
H_2SO_4	H_2	O_2 and H_2O

[1 mark for each correct answer]

c) Potassium is more reactive than hydrogen ***[1 mark]***, so hydrogen is discharged ***[1 mark]***. There are no halide ions ***[1 mark]***, so oxygen and water are discharged ***[1 mark]***.

d) Cathode: $2H^+ + 2e^- \rightarrow H_2$ ***[1 mark]***
Anode: $4OH^- \rightarrow O_2 + 2H_2O + 4e^-$
/ $4OH^- - 4e^- \rightarrow O_2 + 2H_2O$ ***[1 mark]***

Pages 129-130 — Covalent Bonding

1 H–O–H (bent) ***[1 mark]***

H — Cl ***[1 mark]***

2 a) The bonds between the atoms are strong ***[1 mark]***, but the forces between the molecules are weak ***[1 mark]***.

b) The weak forces between the molecules / the intermolecular forces ***[1 mark]***.

3 a) Simple molecular substances have weak forces between molecules ***[1 mark]*** so not much energy is needed to overcome them/they normally have low melting points ***[1 mark]***.

b) Iodine won't conduct electricity ***[1 mark]*** because the I_2 molecules aren't charged / the electrons aren't free to move so can't carry a charge ***[1 mark]***.

4 a) E.g. it contains only non-metals ***[1 mark]*** and there are shared electrons ***[1 mark]***.

b) Any two from, e.g. they don't show how the atoms are arranged in space / they don't show the relative sizes of the atoms ***[2 marks — 1 mark for each correct answer]***.

c) One electron from hydrogen and one from carbon form a shared pair ***[1 mark]*** that are attracted to the nuclei of the carbon and hydrogen atoms ***[1 mark]*** by electrostatic attraction ***[1 mark]***.

5 a) When methane boils, the forces between the molecules are overcome ***[1 mark]*** and it turns from a liquid into a gas ***[1 mark]***. Methane is a smaller molecule then butane ***[1 mark]*** so the forces between the molecules are weaker ***[1 mark]*** and less energy is needed to overcome them ***[1 mark]***.

Chapter C4

b) Carbon needs four more electrons to get a full outer shell, and does this by forming four covalent bonds ***[1 mark]***. Hydrogen only needs one more electron to complete its outer shell, so can only form one covalent bond ***[1 mark]***.

Remember that the outer electron shell in hydrogen only needs two electrons to be filled, not eight like other electron shells.

Page 131 — Empirical Formulas

1 C_2H_6N ***[1 mark]***

2 $10 = 5 \times 2$, so to get from the empirical formula to the molecular formula, multiply all the numbers of atoms by 2: $6 \times 2 = 12$, $5 \times 2 = 10$ and $2 \times 2 = 4$.
So the empirical formula is $C_{12}H_{10}O_4$
[2 marks for the correct answer, otherwise 1 mark for showing the empirical formula should be multiplied by 2.]

3 Emmy is incorrect, e.g. because she not has divided the numbers in the molecular formula by the largest number that will go into both exactly / she has divided both numbers in the formula by 4, but she could have divided by 8 / $8 \div 8 = 1$ and $16 \div 8 = 2$, so the empirical formula is CH_2 ***[1 mark]***.

4 Relative mass of empirical formula is
$(2 \times A_r \text{ of C}) + (A_r \text{ of H}) + (A_r \text{ of F}) = (2 \times 12.0) + 1.0 + 19.0 = 24.0 + 1.0 + 19.0 = 44.0$
M_r of Q $\div$ M_r of empirical formula $= 132.0 \div 44.0 = 3$
So to get the molecular formula, multiply the numbers of atoms in the empirical formula by 3:
molecular formula = $C_6H_3F_3$
[3 marks for correct answer, otherwise 1 mark for finding the relative mass of the empirical formula and 1 mark for dividing the relative mass of the molecular formula by the relative mass of the empirical formula.]

Page 132 — Homologous Series and Alkanes

Warm-up

Hydrocarbon	Not a hydrocarbon
propane ethene C_2H_6 C_2H_4	lithium hydroxide CH_3CH_2Cl hydrochloric acid

1 a) A compound formed from hydrogen and carbon only ***[1 mark]***.

b) i) **B *[1 mark]***

ii) 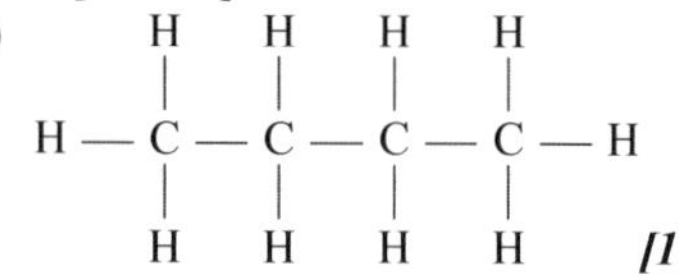

[1 mark]

c) **B**, **D**, and **E** ***[1 mark]***. They have the general formula C_nH_{2n+2} ***[1 mark]***.

d) **E** ***[1 mark]***. Boiling point increases with increasing molecular size/number of carbons ***[1 mark]***.

Pages 133-134 — Fractional Distillation of Crude Oil

1 a) i) A: fractionating column ***[1 mark]***

ii) B: condenser ***[1 mark]***

b) E.g. there is no thermometer ***[1 mark]***, so you cannot monitor the temperature at the top of the fractionating column ***[1 mark]***.

c) E.g. the crude oil substitute is likely to be flammable, so should be kept away from flames / it is easier to control the temperature with an electric heater ***[1 mark]***.

d) A mixture of compounds with similar boiling points / similar carbon chain lengths ***[1 mark]***.

2 a) Oil is heated until most has turned to gas ***[1 mark]***. The gases enter a fractionating column which has a temperature gradient ***[1 mark]***. The fractions separate out as longer hydrocarbons with high boiling points turn to liquid and drain out near the bottom of the column ***[1 mark]***, while shorter hydrocarbons with lower boiling points turn to liquid and drain out near the top of the column ***[1 mark]***.

b) alkanes ***[1 mark]***

c) Any one from: e.g. LPG / petrol / kerosene / diesel oil / heavy fuel oil / bitumen ***[1 mark]***.

d) i) triacontane ***[1 mark]***

ii) E.g. The further down the column a fraction is collected, the higher its boiling point ***[1 mark]***. Long hydrocarbons, like triacontane, have higher boiling points than shorter hydrocarbons like heptane ***[1 mark]***. This is because their chains are much longer and there are many more intermolecular forces to break / the intermolecular bonding is stronger ***[1 mark]***. More energy is needed to overcome these forces and turn the hydrocarbons into a gas ***[1 mark]***.

Page 135 — Uses of Crude Oil

1 a) The amount of some fractions produced does not always meet the demand for those products ***[1 mark]***. More of the product can be produced by cracking longer molecules into smaller,
more useful ones ***[1 mark]***.

b) E.g. $C_{10}H_{22} \rightarrow C_7H_{16} + C_3H_6$ ***[1 mark]***

Cracking equations must always be balanced and have a shorter alkane and an alkene on the right-hand side.

2 a) LPG ***[1 mark]*** and petrol ***[1 mark]***.

b) Heavy fuel oil and bitumen molecules can be cracked to produce extra diesel to help meet the demand ***[1 mark]***.

Chapter C4 — Material Choices

Page 136 — Polymers

Warm-up

Polymers are **long** molecules. They are formed from **small** molecules called **monomers**. Polymers are often referred to as **plastics**. Polymers contain **covalent** bonds, but often behave very differently from simple **molecular** substances.

1 How to grade your answer:

Level 0: There is no relevant information. ***[No marks]***

Level 1: Polymer Y is identified as having stronger bonds between the polymer chains than polymer Z, and there is a suggestion of the nature of the different bonding between the chains in the two polymers. ***[1 to 2 marks]***

Level 2: Polymer Y is identified as having stronger bonds between the polymer chains than polymer Z. There is a suggestion of the nature of the different bonding between the chains in the two polymers and a brief description of how these differences can affect the properties of polymers. ***[3 to 4 marks]***

Level 3: Polymer Y is identified as having stronger bonds between the polymer chains than polymer Z. There is a suggestion of the nature of the different bonding between the chains in the two polymers. Each of the differences in their properties is clearly explained in terms of the differences in bonding between the chains. ***[5 to 6 marks]***

Here are some points your answer may include:
The polymers are both made of the same two elements, so the differences in their properties are likely to be due to differences in their structure and bonding.

Chapter C4

The differences in the properties of the polymers suggest that the polymer chains in polymer Y are held together by stronger bonds than the chains in polymer Z.
The chains of polymer Z are probably only held together by weak intermolecular forces, while the chains of polymer Y are probably linked by stronger covalent or ionic bonds/crosslinks. Crosslinks are stronger and require more energy to break them than intermolecular forces. This explains why polymer Y doesn't melt when heated, whereas polymer Z does.
The crosslinks in polymer Y hold the polymer chains in fixed positions in relation to each other. This explains why polymer Y is rigid.
The weak intermolecular forces in polymer Z allow the polymer chains to slide over each other. This explains why polymer Z is flexible.

Page 137 — Giant Covalent Structures

Warm-up 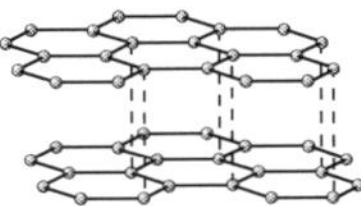

1 a) Structure A: graphene *[1 mark]*
Structure B: diamond *[1 mark]*

b) Graphene/Structure A *[1 mark]*. It has delocalised electrons *[1 mark]* which are free to move through the substance and carry an electric charge *[1 mark]*.

c) To melt them you need to break the strong covalent bonds holding the atoms together *[1 mark]*. This requires a lot of energy *[1 mark]*.

d) Graphite *[1 mark]*. Graphite is made up of sheets of carbon atoms arranged in hexagons *[1 mark]*, with weak forces between the sheets *[1 mark]*. Each carbon atom forms three covalent bonds *[1 mark]*, and has one delocalised electron *[1 mark]*.

Page 138 — Bulk Properties of Materials

Warm-up
Easily reshaped — Particles move without bonds breaking
High tensile strength — Particles held firmly in place
Brittle — Bonds break when particles move

1 Sodium fluoride has electrostatic attractions *[1 mark]* between oppositely charged ions in all directions *[1 mark]*. When molten or dissolved in water, these ions can move and conduct electricity *[1 mark]*. Fluoroethane and poly(fluoroethene) cannot conduct electricity because they do not contain any charged particles that are free to move *[1 mark]*.

2 Black phosphorus is likely to have the highest melting point *[1 mark]* because to melt it you have to break the strong covalent bonds holding the atoms together *[1 mark]*, whereas to melt white phosphorus you only need to break the weak intermolecular forces that hold the molecules together *[1 mark]*.

Pages 139-140 — Types of Materials and Their Uses

1 a) Glass — Ceramic, Polystyrene — Polymer,
Zinc — Metal, Fibreglass — Composite
[4 marks for all four correct answers, otherwise 2 marks for two correct answers.]

b) Composite materials are made of one material embedded in another *[1 mark]*. The properties of a composite depend on the properties of the materials it is made from *[1 mark]*.

2 a) oxidation *[1 mark]*

b) Iron atoms lose electrons and oxygen atoms gain electrons / electrons are transferred from iron to oxygen *[1 mark]*, forming positive iron ions and negative oxygen ions *[1 mark]*.

c) The oil creates a barrier *[1 mark]* which prevents the chain from coming into contact with oxygen in the air *[1 mark]*.

3 a) E.g. The hockey stick needs to be strong to withstand forces applied during the game. Carbon fibre and steel have the greatest strength. The stick needs to be lightweight. Carbon fibre has a much lower density than steel so would be much lighter. Carbon fibre is also resistant to corrosion, which is important if used in the rain. Though carbon fibre is expensive, because the hockey stick is a professional hockey stick, the cost of the stick can be high, so carbon fibre would be the best choice.
[1 mark for each valid comparison between properties from the table, up to a total of 3 marks. 1 mark for choosing a material and giving suitable justification of the choice.]

b) E.g. Bridges need to be strong and, from the choice, steel and carbon fibre are the strongest materials. Bridges are big structures so the cost of the material should be kept down and steel is much cheaper than carbon fibre. Steel is also not too heavy, so a steel bridge won't be too difficult to support *[1 mark]*. Bridges also need to be resistant to corrosion, and steel can be protected to prevent it corroding, so steel would be the best choice.
[1 mark for each valid comparison between properties from the table, up to a total of 3 marks. 1 mark for choosing a material and giving suitable justification of the choice.]

c) E.g. pipes need to have a good resistance to corrosion, so PVC, carbon fibre and lead would be good choices. However PVC is a lot cheaper than lead and carbon fibre. PVC is also lightweight, which allows the pipes to be mounted on houses. The strength of the material is not an important factor, so the low strength of PVC is not an issue. Overall, PVC would be the best choice.
[1 mark for each valid comparison between properties from the table, up to a total of 3 marks. 1 mark for choosing a material and giving suitable justification of the choice.]

Page 141 — Reuse and Recycling

1 a) Material B. Only a small amount of energy is needed to recycle it whereas a lot of energy is needed to extract it *[1 mark]*. Material B also has limited availability, so in the long term it may run out if it is not recycled *[1 mark]*.

b) How to grade your answer:
Level 0: There is no relevant information. *[No marks]*
Level 1: Some understanding of the advantages of recycling and the disadvantages of sending waste to landfill. *[1 to 2 marks]*
Level 2: A clear understanding of the advantages of recycling and the disadvantages of sending waste to landfill. *[3 to 4 marks]*
Level 3: A clear understanding and further discussion of the advantages of recycling and the disadvantages of sending waste to landfill. *[5 to 6 marks]*
Here are some points your answer may include:
Sending PET bottles to landfill takes up lots of space.
Sending PET bottles to landfill pollutes the area.
Sending PET bottles to landfill means that more needs to be made from scratch.
Recycling PET uses fewer resources than manufacturing new PET.
PET is made from alkenes that come from crude oil.
Crude oil is a finite resource and non-renewable so needs to be conserved.
Producing PET from scratch requires distillation and cracking of crude oil, which uses lots of energy — this energy is likely to come from burning crude oil fractions.
Burning the crude oil for energy causes pollution.

Chapter C5

Recycling PET uses less energy than manufacturing new PET.

c) Any two from: e.g. recycling may require more resources than making new material from scratch / recycling the material may require more energy than making new material from scratch / recycling the material may be too expensive / there might not be enough of the material thrown away for it to be recycled on an industrial scale / the demand for the products made from the recycled material may be low ***[1 mark for each correct answer]***.

Pages 142-143 — Life Cycle Assessments

Warm-up

Getting the Raw Materials — Coal being mined from the ground.
Manufacturing and Packaging — Books being made from wood pulp.
Using the Product — A car using fuel while driving.
Product Disposal — Plastic bags going on to landfill.

1 a) A life cycle assessment looks at each stage of the life of a product to work out the potential environmental impact at each stage ***[1 mark]***.

b) Timber is the better choice. Timber comes from a renewable source and so is sustainable ***[1 mark]***, whereas polypropene comes from crude oil which is non-renewable and so is not sustainable ***[1 mark]***. The energy cost to extract timber from trees is also much lower than to make polypropene, meaning that less energy, from e.g. crude oil, is used, making the process more sustainable ***[1 mark]***.

c) Any two from: e.g. how much waste is produced by the process / how much pollution the manufacturing process makes / how long each chair lasts / how much water the process uses ***[1 mark for each correct answer]***.

2 a) E.g. extracting iron from its ore uses a lot of energy / extracting iron from its ore creates pollution ***[1 mark for each correct answer, up to a maximum of 2 marks]***.

b) Advantage: e.g. the energy released can be used to generate electricity ***[1 mark]***.
Disadvantage: e.g. incineration causes air pollution ***[1 mark]***.

c) E.g. by recycling it ***[1 mark]***.

3 E.g. toy A has the highest CO_2 emissions, solvent use and energy consumption, so toy A would have the highest environmental impact ***[1 mark]***. Toy B has the second lowest CO_2 emissions and the second lowest solvent use, but uses the second highest amount of energy, so it would have a medium impact / a higher impact than D, but a lower impact than A or C ***[1 mark]***. Toy C has the second highest CO_2 emissions and solvent use, but the lowest energy consumption, so would have a medium impact / a lower impact than A, but a higher impact than B or D ***[1 mark]***. Toy D has the lowest CO_2 emissions, the lowest solvent use and the second lowest energy consumption, so would have the lowest environmental impact ***[1 mark]***.

Pages 144-145 — Nanoparticles

1 Nanoparticles are 1-100 nm in size ***[1 mark]***

2 Any two from e.g.: nanoparticles are so small that they could penetrate into cells and cause unexpected side effects / the effects of nanoparticles on the human body are largely unknown / there has not been time to investigate the long-term impacts of nanoparticles on human health ***[1 mark for each correct answer]***.

3 a) Material: carbon nanotubes ***[1 mark]***
Reason: e.g. the carbon nanotubes trap the drug molecules inside, and release them when they're at the right place in the body ***[1 mark]***.

b) Material: silver ***[1 mark]***
Reason: e.g. silver nanoparticles are antibacterial, so will help to kill any bacteria that are in the water ***[1 mark]***.

c) Material: carbon nanotubes ***[1 mark]***
Reason: e.g. carbon nanotubes are strong, so will strengthen the sports equipment, but they are also light, so won't add much weight to the equipment ***[1 mark]***.

4 a) $10 \text{ nm} \times 10 \text{ nm} \times 10 \text{ nm} = \mathbf{1000 \text{ nm}^3}$ ***[1 mark]***

b) Area of one side = $10 \text{ nm} \times 10 \text{ nm} = 100 \text{ nm}^2$
A cube has six sides, so total surface area = $6 \times 100 \text{ nm}^2$ = $\mathbf{600 \text{ nm}^2}$ ***[2 marks for correct answer, otherwise 1 mark for the area of one side.]***

c) Surface area to volume ratio = 600 : 1000 = 3 : 5 ***[1 mark]***

d) Volume = $1 \text{ nm} \times 1 \text{ nm} \times 1 \text{ nm} = 1 \text{ nm}^3$
Surface area of one side = $1 \text{ nm} \times 1 \text{ nm} = 1 \text{ nm}^2$
Total surface area of cube = $6 \times 1 \text{ nm}^2 = 6 \text{ nm}^2$
Surface area to volume ratio = 6 : 1
[4 marks for correct answer, otherwise 1 mark for correct volume, 1 mark for correct surface area of one side, 1 mark for correct total surface area.]

e) Surface area to volume ratio = 6 : 1, so if volume = 500 nm^3, surface area = $6 \times 500 = \mathbf{3000 \text{ nm}^2}$ ***[1 mark]***

5 E.g. the surface area to volume ratio ***[1 mark]*** of nanoparticles is much higher than that of larger particles ***[1 mark]***. This gives nanoparticles different qualities because a much greater proportion of their atoms are available to interact with other substances ***[1 mark]***.

Chapter C5 — Chemical Analysis

Page 146 — Purity and Mixtures

1 The scientific definition of a pure substance is one that contains only one element or compound ***[1 mark]***. Although it is labelled 'pure', Stanley's spring water is likely to contain traces of other compounds or elements as well as water molecules (so it will not fit the scientific definition of 'pure water') ***[1 mark]***.

2 E.g. The melting point of an impure substance is lower than the melting point of the pure substance ***[1 mark]***, so the pure sample will be the one with the higher melting point ***[1 mark]***. / The pure substance will melt at a specific temperature ***[1 mark]***, whereas the impure substance will melt over a wider range of temperatures ***[1 mark]***.

3 a) A formulation is a mixture with a precise purpose in which each component is present in a measured quantity ***[1 mark]***.

b) total number of parts in the ratio = 15 + 3 + 2 = 20
proportion of charcoal in gunpowder = $\frac{3}{20}$
mass of charcoal in 40 g of gunpowder = $\frac{3}{20} \times 40 = 6$ g
[3 marks for correct answer, otherwise 1 mark for a correct method to find the proportion of charcoal and 1 mark for a correct method to find the mass of charcoal using the proportion.]

Pages 147-148 — Chromatography

1 a) ethanol ***[1 mark]***

b) The chromatogram suggests there are at least two components in the mixture ***[1 mark]***, since the mixture has separated into two spots ***[1 mark]***.

c) Distance from baseline to spot B = 0.8 cm / 8 mm
Distance from baseline to solvent front = 4.0 cm / 40 mm
Rf = distance travelled by solute ÷ distance travelled by solvent = 0.8 ÷ 4.0 (or 8 ÷ 40) = **0.2**
[2 marks for correct answer, otherwise 1 mark for correctly measuring distances.]

Chapter C5

d) Olivia could re-run the experiment with spots of the pure chemicals alongside the mixture / analyse samples of each of the pure chemicals using paper chromatography, under the same conditions as the mixture ***[1 mark]***. The Rf values of / distance travelled by each spot in the mixture will match the Rf values of / distance travelled by the pure sample of the chemical responsible for that spot ***[1 mark]***.

2 a) Draw a line in pencil near the bottom of a piece of chromatography paper ***[1 mark]***. Place a small spot of the ink and each dye on the line ***[1 mark]***. Pour a shallow layer of water / solvent into a beaker and place the chromatography paper in the beaker ***[1 mark]***. The water should be below the pencil line and the ink/dye spots ***[1 mark]***. Place a lid on the beaker and leave until the water has risen close to the top of the paper ***[1 mark]***.

b) E.g. the ink has a spot at the same height as dye B, so dye B could be in the ink ***[1 mark]***. The ink has a spot at the same height as dyes C and E, so either (or both) of these dyes could be in the ink ***[1 mark]***. The ink has no spot at the same height as dyes A and D, so these dyes are not in the ink ***[1 mark]***. The ink has a spot with a height different to all of the dyes, so it must also contain at least one other dye ***[1 mark]***.

c) E.g. use a locating agent on the completed chromatogram / spray ninhydrin solution on the completed chromatogram / dip the completed chromatogram into a jar containing a few iodine crystals ***[1 mark]***.

Pages 149-150 — Separating Mixtures

1 How to grade your answer:

Level 0: There is no relevant information. ***[No marks]***

Level 1: A method is described which would allow you to obtain a pure sample of only one of the components. The points made are basic and not linked together. ***[1 to 2 marks]***

Level 2: A method is described which would allow you to obtain pure samples of both components, but some details may be missing or incorrect. Some of the points made are linked together. ***[3 to 4 marks]***

Level 3: A method is described clearly and in full, which would allow you to obtain pure samples of both components. The points made are well-linked and the answer has a clear and logical structure. ***[5 to 6 marks]***

Here are some points your answer may include:

Mix the powder with water. This will dissolve the potassium iodide, but not the barium sulfate.

Filter the mixture through a filter paper in a funnel.

The potassium iodide solution will pass through the paper and can be collected in a flask.

The solid barium sulfate will be left in the filter paper.

The solid barium sulfate can be washed with water to remove any traces of potassium iodide and then dried in a drying oven / desiccator / warm place.

The remaining liquid part of the mixture will be a solution of potassium iodide.

To obtain pure potassium iodide from this solution, you can use crystallisation.

Gently heat the solution in an evaporation dish until some of the water has evaporated / until crystals start to form.

Allow the solution to cool, then filter out the crystals.

Dry the crystals by leaving them in a warm place / using a drying oven / using a desiccator.

2 a) Filtration ***[1 mark]*** would separate sodium chloride and ethanol, as the liquid ethanol would flow through the filter paper, leaving behind the solid sodium chloride ***[1 mark]***. However, a mixture of sodium chloride and water is a solution, so both the water and dissolved sodium chloride would pass through the filter paper ***[1 mark]***.

b) E.g. simple distillation ***[1 mark]***. Water and ethanol would both evaporate off and leave behind the solid sodium chloride ***[1 mark]***.

3 The difference in the boiling points of cyclohexane and cyclopentane is quite large, so you could separate them using simple distillation ***[1 mark]***. But the boiling points of cyclohexane and ethyl ethanoate are similar, so you would need to use fractional distillation to separate them ***[1 mark]***.

Page 151 — Relative Mass

Warm-up

F_2 — 38.0, C_2H_6 — 30.0, CaO — 56.1, NaOH — 40.0

1 M_r of $Zn(CN)_2$ = A_r of Zn + (2 × (A_r of C + A_r of N))
= 65.4 + (2 × (12.0 + 14.0))
= 65.4 + (2 × 26.0)
= 65.4 + 52.0 = **117.4**

[2 marks for the correct answer, otherwise 1 mark for writing a correct expression that could be used to calculate the M_r of $Zn(CN)_2$]

2 a) $M_r(MgO) = 24.3 + 16.0 = 40.3$

percentage by mass of magnesium $= \frac{A_r(Mg)}{M_r(MgO)} \times 100$

$= \frac{24.3}{40.3} \times 100 =$ **60.3% (3 s.f.)**

[2 marks for correct answer, otherwise 1 mark for finding correct M_r of MgO]

b) Mass of magnesium ions $= 200 \times \frac{15}{100} =$ **30 g** ***[1 mark]***

Page 152 — Conservation of Mass

1 The total mass of the contents of the flask would be 3.0 + 15.8 = **18.8 g** ***[1 mark]***. This is because, during a reaction, mass is conserved / the total mass of the system doesn't change ***[1 mark]***.

2 a) The total mass of the flask and its contents will decrease over the course of the reaction ***[1 mark]*** as one of the products is hydrogen gas, which is lost from the flask ***[1 mark]***.

b) The total mass of the flask and its contents would stay the same over the course of the reaction ***[1 mark]*** as the reaction is happening in a closed system / any hydrogen gas evolved wouldn't be able to escape, so no reactants are lost ***[1 mark]***.

Pages 153-154 — The Mole

1 6.0×10^{23} atoms ***[1 mark]***

2 $M_r(C_9H_8O_4) = (12.0 \times 9) + (1.0 \times 8) + (16.0 \times 4) = 180$
mass = moles × M_r = 12.5 × 180 = **2250 g**

[2 marks for the correct answer, otherwise 1 mark for the correct M_r of $C_9H_8O_4$]

3 no. molecules = moles × Avogadro's constant
$= 7 \times 6.0 \times 10^{23} = 4.2 \times 10^{24}$

In 1 molecule of ammonia, there are 4 atoms, so in 4.2×10^{24} molecules of ammonia, there must be $4.2 \times 10^{24} \times 4 =$ **1.68×10^{25} atoms**

[2 marks for the correct answer, otherwise 1 mark for correctly calculating the number of ammonia molecules.]

4 From top to bottom:
$1 \div (6.0 \times 10^{23}) =$ **1.7×10^{-24}** ***[1 mark]***
14 ***[1 mark]***
$27 \div (6.0 \times 10^{23}) =$ **4.5×10^{-23}** ***[1 mark]***
18 ***[1 mark]***
$48 \div (6.0 \times 10^{23}) =$ **8.0×10^{-23}** ***[1 mark]***

5 a) $(1.2 \times 10^{25}) \div (6.0 \times 10^{23}) =$ **20 moles** ***[1 mark]***

Chapter C5

b) $(9.3 \times 10^{-23}) \times (6.0 \times 10^{23}) = 55.8$
This atomic mass is closest to iron, so the element must be iron. ***[2 marks for correct answer, otherwise 1 mark for correct atomic mass.]***

6 a) M_r = mass ÷ moles = 343.35 ÷ 3.5 = **98.1** ***[1 mark]***

b) 65% of 98.1 = (98.1 ÷ 100) × 65 = 63.765
Moles of O in 63.765 g = 63.765 ÷ 16 = 3.98... = **4 moles**
[2 marks for correct answer, otherwise 1 mark for correct mass of oxygen in 1 mole of acid.]

c) i) Mass of 1 mole of S = 32.1 g
Mass of 4 moles of O = 16.0 × 4 = 64.0 g
Mass of H in 1 mole of acid = 98.1 – 64.0 – 32.1 = 2.0 g
Moles of H in 2.0 g = 2.0 ÷ 1.0 = **2.0**
[2 marks for correct answer, otherwise 1 mark for correct mass of hydrogen per mole of acid.]

ii) Ratio of S : O : H = 1 : 4 : 2, so formula = $\mathbf{H_2SO_4}$ ***[1 mark]***

If your answer to part a) was incorrect, you'd still get full marks in parts b) and c) if you used that answer but did everything else right.

Pages 155-156 — Calculations Using Balanced Equations

Warm-up

1) decrease 2) increase 3) not change

1 a) magnesium ***[1 mark]***

b) The hydrochloric acid is the limiting reactant ***[1 mark]*** as there is magnesium metal left over in the reaction, showing that it's in excess ***[1 mark]***.

2 $M_r(C_2H_4)$ = (12.0 × 2) + (1.0 × 4) = 28.0
moles = mass ÷ M_r = 53.2 ÷ 28.0 = 1.90 moles
From the reaction equation, 1 mole of C_2H_4 produces 1 mole of CH_3CH_2OH, so 1.90 moles of C_2H_4 will produce 1.90 moles of CH_3CH_2OH.
$M_r(CH_3CH_2OH)$ = 12.0 + (1.0 × 3) + 12.0 + (1.0 × 2) + 16.0 + 1.0 = 46.0
mass = moles × M_r = 1.90 × 46.0 = **87.4 g**
[3 marks for correct answer, otherwise 1 mark for correct M_r of both C_2H_4 and CH_3CH_2OH and 1 mark for correct number of moles of C_2H_4]

3 a) $M_r(O_2)$ = 16.0 × 2 = 32.0
moles = mass ÷ M_r = 128 ÷ 32.0 = 4.00 moles
From the reaction equation, 7 moles of O_2 produces 6 moles of H_2O, so 4.00 moles of O_2 will produce ((4.00 ÷ 7) × 6) = 3.42... moles of H_2O.
$M_r(H_2O)$ = (1.0 × 2) + 16.0 = 18.0
mass = moles × M_r = 3.42... × 18.0 = **61.7 g**
[3 marks for the correct answer, otherwise 1 mark calculating number of moles of O_2 and 1 mark for calculating number of moles of H_2O.]

b) $M_r(CO_2)$ = 12.0 + (16.0 × 2) = 44.0
4.4 tonnes = 4.4 × 1 000 000 = 4 400 000 g
moles = mass ÷ M_r = 4 400 000 ÷ 44.0 = 100 000
For every 4 moles of CO_2 produced, 2 moles of ethane are burnt. So if 100 000 moles of CO_2 are produced, ((100 000 ÷ 4) × 2 =) 50 000 moles of ethane are burnt.
$M_r(C_2H_6)$ = (12.0 × 2) + (1.0 × 6) = 30.0
mass = moles × M_r = 50 000 × 30.0 = 1 500 000 g
1 500 000 g = 1 500 000 ÷ 1 000 000 = **1.5 tonnes**
[3 marks for correct answer, otherwise 1 mark for finding moles of CO_2 and 1 mark for finding mass of C_2H_6 in g.]

4 a) $M_r((NH_2)_2CO)$ = 2 × (14.0 + (1.0 × 2) + 12.0 + 16.0 = 60.0
120.6 tonnes = 120.6 × 1 000 000 = 120 600 000 g
moles = mass ÷ M_r = 120 600 000 ÷ 60 = 2 010 000
From the reaction equation, 1 mole of $(NH_2)_2CO$ is made from 1 mole of CO_2, so making 2 010 000 moles of $(NH_2)_2CO$ will require 2 010 000 moles of CO_2.
$M_r(CO_2)$ = 12.0 + (16.0 × 2) = 44.0
mass = moles × M_r = 2 010 000 × 44.0 = 88 440 000 g
88 440 000 g = 88 440 000 ÷ 1 000 000 = **88.44 tonnes**
[3 marks for correct answer, otherwise 1 mark for finding moles of $(NH_2)_2CO$ and 1 mark for finding mass of CO_2 in g.]

b) $M_r(NH_3)$ = 14.0 + (1.0 × 3) = 17.0
59.5 tonnes = 59.5 × 1 000 000 = 59 500 000 g
moles = mass ÷ M_r = 59 500 000 ÷ 17.0 = 3 500 000
From the reaction equation, 2 moles of NH_3 makes 1 mole of $(NH_2)_2CO$, so 3 500 000 moles of NH_3 will make (3 500 000 ÷ 2 =) 1 750 000 moles of $(NH_2)_2CO$.
From a), $M_r((NH_2)_2CO)$ = 60.0
mass = moles × M_r = 1 750 000 × 60.0 = 105 000 000 g
105 000 000 = 105 000 000 ÷ 1 000 000 = 105 tonnes
difference between masses of $(NH_2)_2CO$ = 120.6 – 105 = **15.6 tonnes**
[4 marks for correct answer, otherwise 1 mark for finding moles of NH_3, 1 mark for finding mass of $(NH_2)_2CO$ in g and 1 mark for finding mass of $(NH_2)_2CO$ in tonnes.]

Pages 157-158 — Calculations Using Moles

1 a) All the carbon in CO_2 (4 moles of C atoms) must have come from A, so must all the hydrogen in 4 moles of H_2O (8 moles of H atoms), so the formula of the hydrocarbon must be C_4H_8
[1 mark for correct number of Cs, 1 mark for correct number of Hs.]

b) $C_4H_8 + \mathbf{6}O_2 \rightarrow \mathbf{4}CO_2 + \mathbf{4}H_2O$ ***[1 mark]***

2 a) 280 – 200 = **80 g** ***[1 mark]***

b) moles = mass ÷ M_r
moles of X = 200 ÷ 40 = 5 moles
moles of O_2 = 80 ÷ (2 × 16) = 2.5 moles
There are twice as many moles of X as O_2, so the reaction must happen in a 2 : 1 ratio of X to O_2.
$2X + O_2 \rightarrow$ X oxide
Since all of the reactants end up in the products, and there are two atoms of X and O on the left-hand side of the equation, the formula of X oxide must be X_1O_1, or XO.
So, balanced equation = $2X + O_2 \rightarrow 2XO$
[4 marks for correct answer, otherwise 1 mark for calculating the moles of X and the moles of O_2 gas, 1 mark for working out the simplest ratio of X : O : X oxide, 1 mark for stating the formula of X oxide.]

You could have done some of the working for this question differently, so don't worry if you've approached it in another way. If your answer is right you'll get full marks anyway. If your answer is wrong, you should get marks for your working, as long as the method you've used is sensible.

3 a) $M_r(H_2O)$ = (1.0 × 2) + 16.0 = 18.0
mass of H_2O = 228.2 – 156.2 = 72.0 g
moles = mass ÷ M_r = 72.0 ÷ 18.0 = **4 moles**
[2 marks for correct answer, otherwise 1 mark for calculating mass of H_2O]

b) From the balanced equation, 2 moles of NaOH produced 2 moles of H_2O. So, if 4 moles of H_2O were produced, 4 moles of NaOH must have been used.
$M_r(NaOH)$ = 23.0 + 16.0 + 1.0 = 40.0
mass = moles × M_r = 4 × 40.0 = **160 g**
[2 marks for correct answer, otherwise 1 mark for calculating the number of moles of NaOH]

Chapter C5

c) Since 160 g of the reactants were NaOH,
mass of acid = 228.2 – 160 = 68.2 g
From the equation, 2 moles of H_2O are produced by 1 mole of H_2X. So, 4 moles of H_2O (from part b) i)) would be produced by 2 moles of H_2X.
M_r = mass ÷ moles = 68.2 ÷ 2 = **34.1**
[3 marks for correct answer, otherwise 1 mark for calculating the mass of the acid and 1 mark for calculating the number of moles of H_2X]

4 E.g. mass of metal halide produced = 3.57 + 15.24 = 18.81 g
moles = mass ÷ M_r
moles of Sn = 3.57 ÷ 118.7 = 0.03 moles
moles of I_2 = 15.24 ÷ 253.8 = 0.06 moles
moles of metal halide = 18.81 ÷ 627 = 0.03
The ratio of Sn : I_2 : metal halide is 0.03 : 0.06 : 0.03.
Dividing all of these by 0.03 gives a ratio of 1 : 2 : 1.
$Sn + 2I_2 \rightarrow$ metal halide
Since all of the reactants end up in the product, and there is one atom of Sn and four atoms of I on the left-hand side of the equation, the formula of the metal halide must be SnI_4.
So, the balanced equation is: $Sn + 2I_2 \rightarrow SnI_4$
[5 marks for correct answer, otherwise 1 mark for calculating the mass of metal halide made, 1 mark for calculating the number of moles of reactants and product, 1 mark for working out the simplest ratio of Sn : I_2 : metal halide, 1 mark for stating the formula of the metal halide.]

Don't worry if you've done the working for this question a bit differently too — as long as your method and answer are correct, you'll get all the marks.

Page 159 — Acids and Alkalis

Warm-up
1) sodium nitrate 2) calcium chloride 3) sodium sulfate
4) potassium chloride 5) calcium nitrate

1 $HNO_3 + LiOH \rightarrow LiNO_3 + H_2O$ ***[1 mark]***

2 a) acid + base → salt + water ***[1 mark]***

b) $H^+ + OH^- \rightarrow H_2O$ ***[1 mark]***

Page 160 — Concentrations

Warm-up
The third beaker (Volume = 0.2 dm^3, Concentration = 35 g/dm^3) should be circled.
You can work out the mass in each beaker using the formula mass = concentration × volume. So from left to right, the beakers contain 0.3 × 20 = 6 g, 0.1 × 45 = 4.5 g and 0.2 × 35 = 7 g of copper sulfate.

1 90 g/dm^3 ***[1 mark]***

2 a) volume in dm^3 = 400 ÷ 1000 = 0.4 dm^3
concentration in g/dm^3 = mass in g ÷ volume in dm^3
= 28 ÷ 0.4 = **70 g/dm^3**
[2 marks for correct answer, otherwise 1 mark for correctly converting volume to dm^3.]

b) The concentration of a solution is the amount of a substance in a given volume of the solution ***[1 mark]***.

3 M_r(LiOH) = 6.9 + 16.0 + 1.0 = 23.9
moles = mass ÷ M_r = 4.78 ÷ 23.9 = 0.20 moles
volume in dm^3 = 250 ÷ 1000 = 0.250 dm^3
concentration in mol/dm^3 = no. of moles ÷ volume in dm^3
= 0.20 ÷ 0.250 = **0.80 mol/dm^3**
[3 marks for correct answer, otherwise 1 mark for calculating number of moles of LiOH and 1 mark for correctly converting volume to dm^3.]

Page 161 — Standard Solutions

1 a) 220 cm^3 = (220 ÷ 1000) dm^3 = 0.220 dm^3
Mass = concentration × volume = 75.0 × 0.220 = **16.5 g**
[1 mark]

b) Dissolving 56 g of copper sulfate in 220 cm^3 of water will make a solution more concentrated than X. ***[1 mark]***

2 a) Moles of Na_2CO_3 = 0.50 mol/dm^3 × 0.50 dm^3 = **0.25 mol** ***[1 mark]***

b) 200 cm^3 = 200 ÷ 1000 = 0.2 dm^3
moles of Na_2CO_3 in 200 cm^3 of 0.30 mol/dm^3 solution
= concentration × volume = 0.30 × 0.2 = 0.06 moles
volume of 0.50 mol/dm^3 solution needed
= number of moles ÷ concentration
= 0.06 ÷ 0.50 = 0.12 dm^3
0.12 dm^3 = 0.12 × 1000 = **120 cm^3**
[3 marks for correct answer, otherwise 1 mark for calculating the required number of moles and 1 mark for a correct conversion from dm^3 to cm^3.]

You could have done some of the working for this question differently. If your answer is right you'll get full marks anyway, and if your answer is wrong, you can still get marks for using a sensible method.

Pages 162-164 — Titrations

Warm-up:

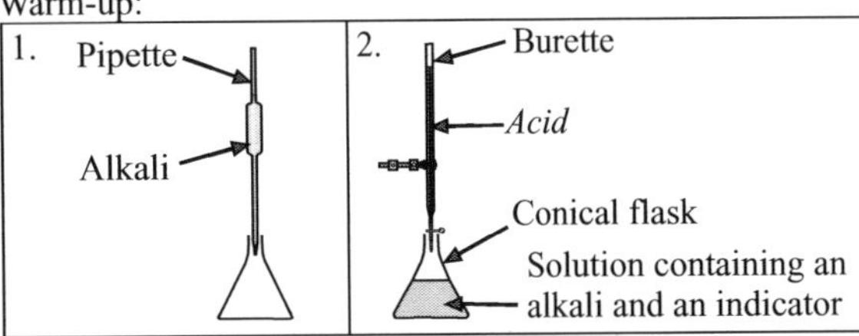

1 a) Universal indicator is the most suitable indicator for use in titrations ***[1 mark]***.

b) A burette allows an acid/alkali to be added to a solution drop by drop ***[1 mark]*** which helps determine the end-point more accurately ***[1 mark]***.

c) The titration should be repeated several times to achieve several consistent readings ***[1 mark]***. The mean reading should be used to calculate the concentration ***[1 mark]***.

2 16.7 g/dm^3 ***[1 mark]***
2 moles of KOH reacts with 1 mole of H_2SO_4.
So, 0.00850 mol KOH reacts with 0.00425 mol H_2SO_4.
Concentration = moles ÷ volume
Concentration of H_2SO_4 = 0.00425 ÷ 0.0250 = 0.170 mol/dm^3
Concentration (g/dm^3) = concentration (mol/dm^3) × M_r
= 0.170 × 98.1 = ***16.7 g/dm^3***

3 a) How to grade your answer:
Level 0: There is no relevant information. ***[No marks]***
Level 1: There is a brief explanation of how to carry a titration but it is not detailed and little technical equipment is mentioned. ***[1 to 2 marks]***
Level 2: There is an explanation of how to carry out a titration and some of the equipment required, but there are limited details. ***[3 to 4 marks]***
Level 3: There is a clear and detailed explanation of how to carry out a titration and all the equipment needed is clearly included. ***[5 to 6 marks]***
Here are some points your answer may include:
Measure out a known volume of the sodium hydroxide solution using a pipette and put it in a conical flask.
Add a few drops of an indicator to the sodium hydroxide solution.
Use the burette to add the sulfuric acid to the sodium hydroxide solution, swirling the conical flask regularly.
Stop the titration when the indicator changes colour. This is when the sodium hydroxide solution is completely neutralised.
Record the volume of sulfuric acid required to cause this colour change.

Repeat the titration with the same volume of sodium hydroxide solution, but add the acid one drop at a time, close to the end-point.
Record the exact volume of sulfuric acid required to neutralise the sodium hydroxide solution.
Repeat the titration several times until you have several consistent readings.
Calculate the mean of the results, ignoring any anomalous results.

b) Moles = concentration × volume
Moles of H_2SO_4 = 0.200 × (22.5 ÷ 1000) = 0.00450 moles
1 mole of H_2SO_4 reacts with 2 moles of NaOH.
So, 0.00450 moles of H_2SO_4 reacts with (0.00450 × 2) = 0.00900 moles of NaOH
Concentration of NaOH = 0.00900 ÷ (25.0 ÷ 1000)
= **0.360 mol/dm³**
[3 marks for correct answer, otherwise 1 mark for correct moles of H_2SO_4 and 1 mark for correct moles of NaOH.]

4 a) Any two from: e.g. multiple readings allow you to spot anomalous results. / Getting the same result more than once shows results are repeatable. / Getting multiple results in close agreement with each other shows they are precise. / Taking a mean of several results can help to cancel out random errors (and therefore improve accuracy).
[1 mark for each correct reason, up to a maximum of 2 marks.]

b) Mean vol. of HCl = (12.50 + 12.55 + 12.45) ÷ 3 = **12.50 cm³**
[2 marks for correct answer, otherwise 1 mark for correct equation to calculate the mean]

c) Volume of HCl = 12.50 cm³ ÷ 1000 = 0.01250 dm³
Volume of Na_2CO_3 = 25.0 cm³ ÷ 1000 = 0.0250 dm³
Moles of HCl = 0.0125 dm³ × 1.00 mol/dm³ = 0.0125 mol
Molar ratio of HCl : Na_2CO_3 = 2:1
Moles of Na_2CO_3 = 0.01250 mol ÷ 2 = 0.006250 mol
Concentration of Na_2CO_3 = 0.006250 mol ÷ 0.0250 dm³
= **0.250 mol/dm³**
[6 marks for correct answer, otherwise 1 mark for volumes of HCl and Na_2CO_3 in dm³, 1 mark for correct equation to calculate moles, 1 mark for moles of HCl, 1 mark for moles of Na_2CO_3 and 1 mark for correct equation to calculate concentration]

If answer to part b) is incorrect, but your working is correct here, you still get all the marks, even if you got a different answer.

Chapter C6 — Making Useful Chemicals

Page 165 — Acids, Alkalis and pH

Warm-up
Universal indicator will turn **red** in strongly acidic solutions and **purple** in strongly alkaline solutions. In a **neutral** solution, universal indicator will be green. A pH probe attached to a pH meter is **more** accurate than universal indicator as it displays a numerical value for pH.

1 a) 0 – 14 ***[1 mark]***
b) A dye that changes colour ***[1 mark]*** depending on whether it's above or below a certain pH ***[1 mark]***.

2 You should wash a pH probe with a weak acid in between readings ***[1 mark]***.

3 a) 3 ***[1 mark]***
b) E.g. the pH will increase by 1 ***[1 mark]***.

Page 166 — Strong and Weak Acids

1 a) $HCOOH \rightleftharpoons HCOO^- + H^+$ ***[1 mark for correct equation, 1 mark for arrow showing reversible reaction.]***

b) The reaction will take place faster with the strong acid. During the reaction, zinc reacts with H^+ ions in the solution, so the higher the concentration of H^+ ions, the faster the reaction ***[1 mark]***. Strong acids dissociate more than weak acids, so the concentration of H^+ ions will be higher for a strong acid of the same concentration as the methanoic acid, a weak acid ***[1 mark]***.

2 Beaker X: 0.002 mol/dm³ HCl
Beaker Y: 4.0 mol/dm³ CH_3COOH ***[1 mark]***

3 Dissolve more solid acid in the sample ***[1 mark]***.

Page 167 — Reactions of Acids

1 a) A salt and water ***[1 mark]***.
b) neutralisation ***[1 mark]***

2 From top to bottom: $Zn(NO_3)_2$ ***[1 mark]***, $CaSO_4$ ***[1 mark]***, Na_2SO_4 ***[1 mark]***, KCl ***[1 mark]***

3 a) carbon dioxide ***[1 mark]***
b) $ZnCO_3 + 2HCl \rightarrow ZnCl_2 + H_2O + CO_2$
[2 marks for all formulas correct and a correctly-balanced equation, otherwise 1 mark for correct formulas in an unbalanced equation.]
c) zinc chloride ***[1 mark]***

Pages 168-170 — Making Salts

Warm-up
titration, distillation

1 $Pb(NO_3)_{2\,(aq)} + 2NaCl_{(aq)} \rightarrow PbCl_{2\,(s)} + 2NaNO_{3\,(aq)}$
[1 mark]

2 a) hydrochloric acid ***[1 mark]***
b) Jeremy has poured too much solution into the funnel / the level of the solution goes above the filter paper ***[1 mark]***. This means that some of the solid can pass down the sides of the filter paper and into the conical flask below, reducing the amount of solid that's extracted from the solution ***[1 mark]***.

3 a) $Fe(OH)_3$ ***[1 mark]***
b) i) E.g. to make sure that all of the precipitate is transferred from the beaker to the funnel / to make sure she doesn't lose any of the product ***[1 mark]***.
ii) E.g. scrape the product on to a clean piece of filter paper and dry in an oven / desiccator / warm place ***[1 mark]***.

4 a) 4, 3, 1, 5, 2 ***[2 marks for all five steps in the correct order, otherwise 1 mark for three steps in the correct positions.]***
b) $Mg(OH)_{2\,(s)} + H_2SO_{4\,(aq)} \rightarrow MgSO_{4\,(aq)} + 2H_2O_{(l)}$
[1 mark for all formulas correct, 1 mark for a correctly-balanced equation and 1 mark for correct state symbols.]

5 a) It dissolves in water ***[1 mark]***.
b) $Na_2CO_3 + 2HNO_3 \rightarrow 2NaNO_3 + H_2O + CO_2$
[2 marks for all formulas correct and a correctly-balanced equation, otherwise 1 mark for correct formulas in an unbalanced equation.]
c) No, because the salt will be contaminated by the indicator ***[1 mark]***.

6 a) $H_2SO_4 + CuO \rightarrow CuSO_4 + H_2O$
[2 marks for all formulas correct and a correctly-balanced equation, otherwise 1 mark for correct formulas in an unbalanced equation.]
b) How to grade your answer:
Level 0: There is no relevant information. ***[No marks]***
Level 1: There is a brief explanation of how to prepare the salt but no details are given. The points made are basic and not linked together. ***[1 to 2 marks]***
Level 2: There is some explanation of how to prepare the salt, including necessary equipment and how to isolate the salt, but the method is missing key details. Some of the points made are linked together. ***[3 to 4 marks]***

Chapter C6

Level 3: There is a clear and detailed explanation of how to produce and extract a pure sample of the salt. The points made are well-linked and the answer has a clear and logical structure. ***[5 to 6 marks]***

Here are some points your answer may include:
Warm the sulfuric acid in a water bath.
Warm the acid in a fume cupboard to avoid releasing acid fumes into the room.
Add copper oxide to the acid.
When the reaction is complete and the copper oxide is in excess, the solid copper oxide will sink to the bottom.
Filter the reaction mixture to remove the excess copper oxide.
Heat the remaining solution gently (using a Bunsen burner) to evaporate off some of the water.
Leave the solution to cool and allow the salt to crystallise.
Filter off the solid salt and leave the crystals to dry.

Pages 171-172 — Rates of Reactions

1 a) Decreasing the concentration of the solution ***[1 mark]***.
b) activation energy ***[1 mark]***
2 a) i) Produced most product: C ***[1 mark]***
ii) Finished first: B ***[1 mark]***
iii) Started at the slowest rate: A ***[1 mark]***
b)

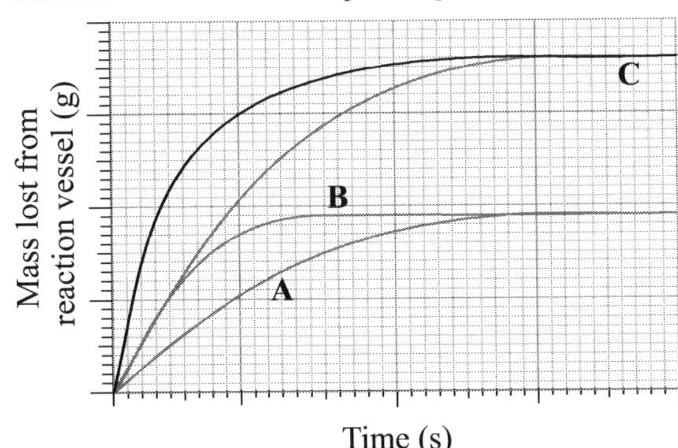

[1 mark for curve with steeper gradient than curve C at the start of the reaction, 1 mark for curve reaching the final volume earlier than curve C, 1 mark for final volume being the same as for curve C.]

3 a) E.g. there may be extra restrictions on reaction conditions such as temperature and pH to make sure that the enzyme will work better ***[1 mark]***.
b) A: reactants ***[1 mark]***
B: activation energy with a catalyst ***[1 mark]***
C: activation energy without a catalyst ***[1 mark]***
D: products ***[1 mark]***
c) 34 °C ***[1 mark]***

The temperature where the rate of reaction is fastest is the point at which the curve is highest.

4 a) E.g. increasing the volume of the reaction vessel would decrease the pressure of the reacting gases ***[1 mark]***. So the particles would be more spread out and would collide less frequently ***[1 mark]***, so the reaction rate would decrease ***[1 mark]***.
b) E.g. increasing the temperature would cause the particles to move faster, so the frequency of collisions would increase ***[1 mark]***. It would also increase the energy of the collisions, so more collisions would be successful ***[1 mark]***. This means the reaction rate would increase ***[1 mark]***.

Pages 173-174 — Reaction Rate Experiments

1 a) time taken for the solution to go cloudy ***[1 mark]***
b) temperature ***[1 mark]***
c) Any one from: e.g. the concentration of the reactants / the volume of the reactants / the depth of the reaction mixture ***[1 mark]***.
d) It would be more accurate to measure the volume of gas produced ***[1 mark]***, as this method is less subjective ***[1 mark]***.
2 a) E.g. remove the two solutions from the water bath and immediately mix the solutions in a conical flask ***[1 mark]***. Connect the flask to a gas syringe/up-turned measuring cylinder filled with water / place the flask on a mass balance ***[1 mark]*** and monitor the volume of gas produced / mass of gas lost at regular intervals ***[1 mark]***.
b) Rate = amount of product formed ÷ time = 10.60 ÷ 40.0
= **0.265** ***[2 marks for correct answer, otherwise 1 mark for correct equation to calculate rate.]***
Units = units of amount of product ÷ units of time
= $cm^3 \div s$ = $\mathbf{cm^3/s}$ ***[1 mark]***

3 a)

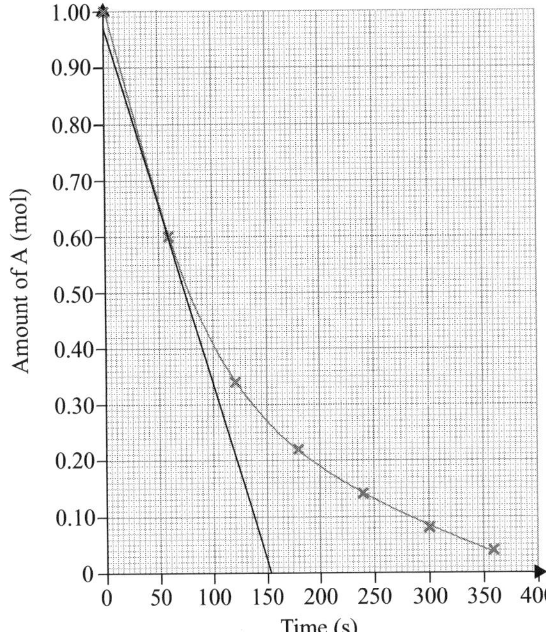

Gradient = $\frac{\text{change in } y}{\text{change in } x} = \frac{0.97}{153}$ = **0.0063 mol/s**
(allow between 0.0053 mol/s and 0.0073 mol/s)
[4 marks for correct answer, otherwise 1 mark for correctly drawn tangent to curve drawn at 50 s, 1 mark for answer to 2 s.f., 1 mark for correct units]

b)

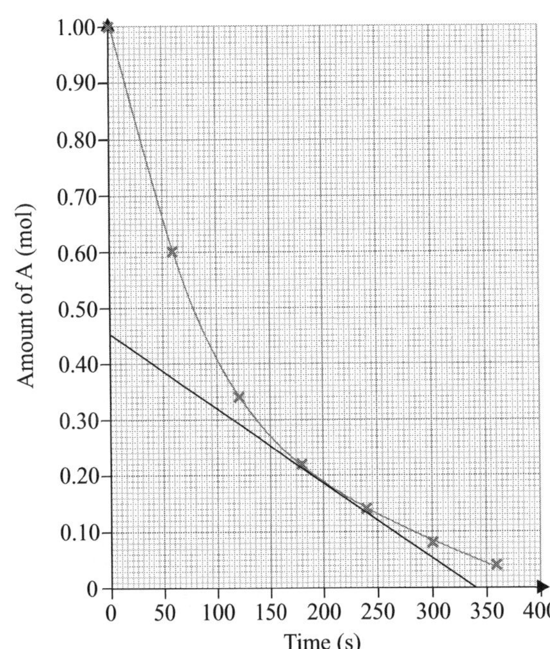

Chapter P1

Gradient = $\frac{\text{change in } y}{\text{change in } x} = \frac{0.45}{340}$ = **0.0013 mol/s**
(allow between 0.0010 mol/s and 0.0018 mol/s)
[4 marks for correct answer, otherwise 1 mark for correctly drawn tangent to curve drawn at 200 s, 1 mark for answer to 2 s.f., 1 mark for correct units]

c) colorimeter ***[1 mark]***

Page 175 — Dynamic Equilibrium

Warm-up

In a reversible reaction, as the concentrations of the reactants fall, the rate of the forward reaction **decreases** and as the concentrations of the products rise, the rate of the backward reaction **increases**. When both the forward and backward reactions are going at **the same rate**, they are at equilibrium. At this point, the concentrations of the reactants and products will **not change**.

1 a) At dynamic equilibrium, the rates of the forward and the backward reactions are equal/the same ***[1 mark]*** and the concentrations of the reactants and products at equilibrium do not change ***[1 mark]***.

b) A closed system is a system where none of the reactants or products can escape ***[1 mark]***.

2 a) That the reaction is reversible / can go both ways ***[1 mark]***.

b) The system has reached equilibrium ***[1 mark]***. This mixture contains both blue copper(II) ions and the yellow copper compound, so the colours mix to form green ***[1 mark]***.

Pages 176-177 — Changing the Position of Equilibrium

Warm-up

more reactants, more reactants, more products

1 a) If you change the conditions of a reversible reaction at equilibrium, the system will try to counteract that change ***[1 mark]***.

b) E.g. the temperature / the concentration of the reactants ***[2 marks — 1 mark for each correct answer]***

2 a) At higher temperatures there will be more ICl and less ICl_3 / the equilibrium will shift to the left ***[1 mark]***. This is because the reverse reaction is endothermic so opposes the increase in temperature ***[1 mark]***.

b) There would be more ICl_3 and less ICl ***[1 mark]*** because the increase in pressure ***[1 mark]*** causes the equilibrium position to move to the side with the fewer molecules of gas ***[1 mark]***.

3 a) At higher temperature there's more product (brown NO_2) in the equilibrium mixture ***[1 mark]***. This suggests that the equilibrium has moved to the right/forward direction ***[1 mark]***, so the forward reaction is endothermic ***[1 mark]***.

From Le Chatelier's principle, you know that increasing the temperature will favour the endothermic reaction as the equilibrium tries to oppose the change. So the forward reaction must be endothermic, as there's more NO_2 in the equilibrium mixture at higher temperatures.

b) The mixture would go a darker brown ***[1 mark]***, as the decrease in pressure causes the equilibrium to move to the side with more molecules of gas ***[1 mark]***, meaning more NO_2 is formed ***[1 mark]***.

4 Observation 1: Increasing amounts of red $FeSCN^{2+}$ are formed, so the solution becomes a darker red ***[1 mark]***. When equilibrium is reached, the amount of each substance stops changing, and so does the colour ***[1 mark]***.
Observation 2: The concentration of Fe^{3+} initially increases, so the solution becomes more orangey ***[1 mark]***. The equilibrium then shifts to make more $FeSCN^{2+}$, so the solution becomes darker red in colour ***[1 mark]***.
Observation 3: The concentration of $FeSCN^{2+}$ initially increases, so the solution becomes darker red ***[1 mark]***. The equilibrium then shifts to produce more reactants, so the solution becomes more orangey ***[1 mark]***.

Chapter P1 — Radiation and Waves

Pages 178-179 — Waves

Warm-up

E.g.:

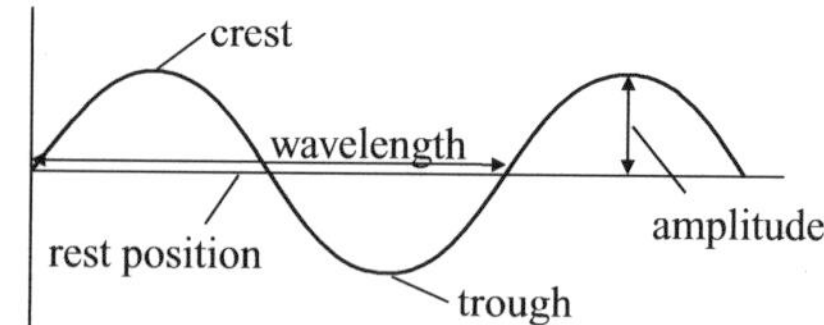

1 sound waves in air ***[1 mark]***

2 E.g. in longitudinal waves, the disturbance of the medium is parallel to the wave's direction of travel ***[1 mark]***, but in transverse waves, the disturbance of the medium is at right angles to the direction of travel ***[1 mark]***.

3 a) E.g:

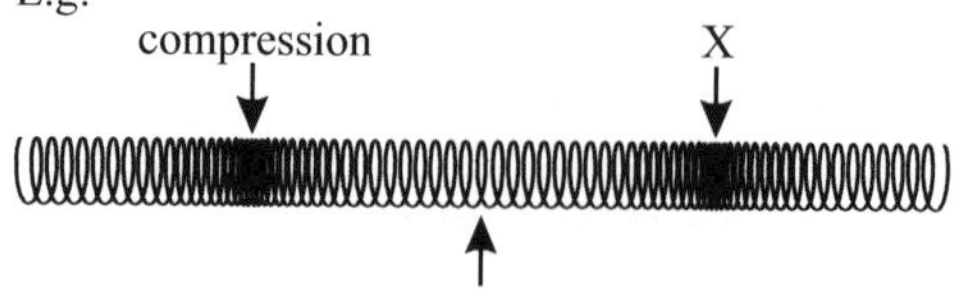

[1 mark for compression labelled at X or location shown and 1 mark for rarefaction labelled at either end of spring or location shown.]

b) Frequency is the number of complete cycles of a wave passing a point per second.
So to find frequency, divide number of complete cycles by the time taken in seconds.
frequency = 400 ÷ 50
= **8 Hz**
[2 marks for correct answer, otherwise 1 mark for correct method.]

4 a) The leaf will not be carried to the edge of the pond. Waves transfer energy, not matter ***[1 mark], so the ripples don't move water or the leaf from one place to another [1 mark]***.

b) 15 ÷ 1000 = 0.015 m
$1.4 \times 10^{-2} \times 1000$ = 14 Hz ***[1 mark]***
$v = f\lambda$ ***[1 mark]*** = 14 × 0.015 ***[1 mark]***
= **0.21 m/s** ***[1 mark]***

5 a) air ***[1 mark]***

b) 2.49 × 1000 = 2490 Hz
$v = f\lambda$ so $\lambda = v \div f$ = 340 ÷ 2490 = 0.1365...
= **0.14 m (to 2 s.f.)**
[4 marks for the correct answer, otherwise 1 mark for correctly converting from kHz to Hz, 1 mark for correctly rearranging and using the equation $v = f\lambda$, 1 mark for correctly calculating a wavelength of 0.1365... m and 1 mark for rounding to 2 s.f.]

c) frequency = 220 Hz
so 220 waves are produced per second.
So, the number of waves produced in 5 s = 220 × 5
= 1100
[2 marks for a correct answer, otherwise 1 mark for correct method.]

You could have also solved this by calculating the period, and dividing 5 s by the period.

Page 180 — Wave Experiments

1 a) Any two from: e.g. the position of the dipper / the position of the cork when she starts timing / the depth of water in the tank / the equipment used ***[2 marks — 1 mark for each correct answer.]***

Chapter P1

b) The result of the third trial is anomalous.
(36 + 33 + 33 + 42) ÷ 4 = **36 s**
[2 marks for a correct answer, otherwise 1 mark for correctly identifying the anomalous result.]

c) Frequency = number of waves in one second, so divide the number of waves by the time taken.
frequency = 30 ÷ 36
= 0.83333....
= **0.83 Hz (to 2 s.f.)**
[3 marks for correct answer, otherwise 1 mark for correct calculation and 1 mark for correct unrounded answer]

d) E.g. one of them could use a pencil to trace the progress of a ripple through the tank on a piece of paper for a fixed distance ***[1 mark]***, while the other student measures the time taken to travel this distance with a stopwatch ***[1 mark]***. The formula speed = distance ÷ time can be used to calculate the wave speed ***[1 mark]***.

Page 181 — Reflection and Refraction

Warm-up
wave is reflected — it bounces back off the material
wave is absorbed — it transfers all its energy to the material
wave is transmitted — it passes through the material

1 a) refraction ***[1 mark]***
b) 90° ***[1 mark]***

2 a) Section 2 is shallower than Section 1 ***[1 mark]***.
The wave has bent towards the normal, and its wavelength has decreased, so the speed of the wave has decreased and the water must be shallower.

b) As the water wave enters Section 2, the frequency of the wave remains the same ***[1 mark]*** but its wavelength decreases ***[1 mark]***.

Pages 182-183 — Reflection and Refraction Experiments

1 a)

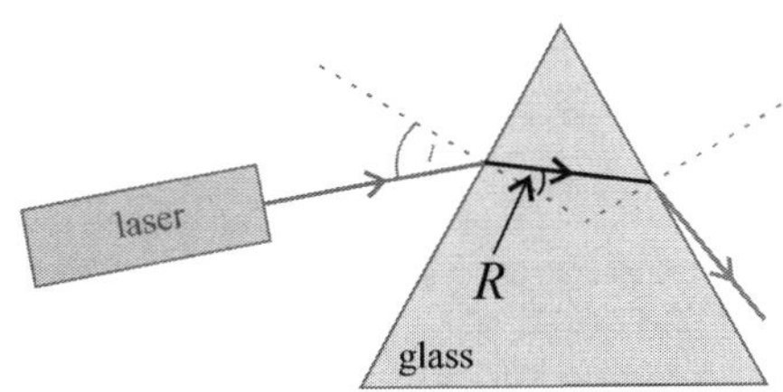

[1 mark for drawing the path of the ray through the prism and marking angle R, as shown in the diagram above.]

b) Plastic ***[1 mark]***. It has the largest angle of refraction ***[1 mark]***, which means the ray has been bent the least by the plastic prism, and so the change of speed of the ray is the smallest ***[1 mark]***.

c) E.g. a bar chart ***[1 mark]*** because the data is categoric ***[1 mark]***.

2 a)

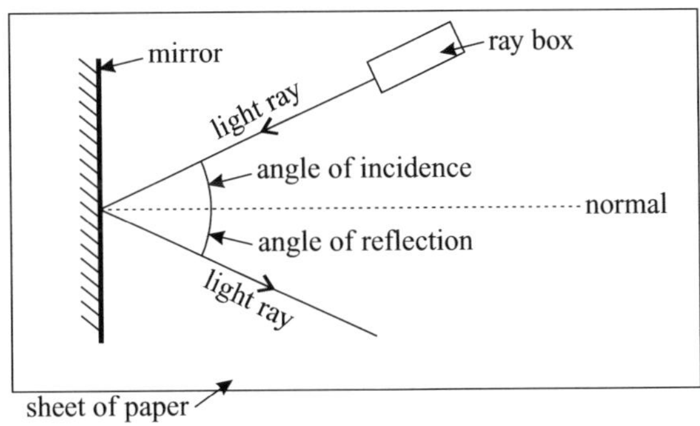

[1 mark for diagram showing a ray box positioned at an angle to a mirror. 1 mark for normal and angles of incidence and reflection correctly labelled.]

Stand a mirror on a piece of paper with a dotted line (the normal) drawn at 90° to the mirror's surface ***[1 mark]***. Shine a ray of light towards the point where the normal meets the mirror ***[1 mark]***. Trace the light ray, and use a protractor to measure the angles of incidence and refraction and record these values ***[1 mark]***. Repeat this, varying the angle between the ray and the normal each time ***[1 mark]***.

b) A ray box was used to provide a thin beam of light ***[1 mark]*** so that the angles of incidence and reflection could be easily and accurately measured ***[1 mark]***.

c) A systematic error ***[1 mark]***. E.g. he may have drawn the normal incorrectly / the surface of the mirror may not be flat ***[1 mark]***.

Page 184 — The Electromagnetic Spectrum

Warm-up
False, True, True

1 The second part of Sonya's statement is incorrect because human eyes can only detect visible light, which is a small range of frequencies in the electromagnetic spectrum ***[1 mark]***.

2 On Earth, oxygen in the upper atmosphere absorbs UV radiation and forms ozone ***[1 mark]***. Ozone can absorb the ionising UV radiation from the Sun ***[1 mark]***. This prevents ionising UV radiation from reaching humans on the Earth's surface ***[1 mark]***. This does not happen on the Moon, as the moon has no atmosphere, and the harmful UV radiation will reach the Moon's surface ***[1 mark]***.

Page 185 — Energy Levels and Ionisation

Warm-up
The electrons around an atom are at <u>different</u> distances from the nucleus.
An electron moves <u>further from</u> the nucleus when it absorbs EM radiation.
An electron that moves closer to the nucleus will <u>release</u> radiation.

1 a) An electron has been removed from it ***[1 mark]***.
b) Any two from: e.g. damage to skin cells ***[1 mark]*** / skin cancer ***[1 mark]*** / damage to eyes/eye conditions ***[1 mark]***.
c) Any one from: X-rays / gamma radiation ***[1 mark]***

2 a) Excited electrons fall back down to their original energy level ***[1 mark]***. The extra energy is released as radiation ***[1 mark]***.
b) The electrons fall down between different energy levels in the mercury and phosphorus atoms when they emit radiation ***[1 mark]***, releasing different amounts of energy and so different frequencies of radiation ***[1 mark]***. The part of the electromagnetic spectrum that the radiation is from depends on the frequency of the radiation ***[1 mark]***.

Pages 186-187 — Uses of EM Radiation

1 a) satellite communications ***[1 mark]***
b) E.g. cooking food (in microwave ovens) ***[1 mark]***.

2 E.g: gamma rays kill microbes when they are absorbed ***[1 mark]***. Gamma rays pass through materials and so reach crevices which would otherwise be difficult to clean ***[1 mark]***.

3 a) X-rays are transmitted by soft tissues/flesh ***[1 mark]***, but are blocked/absorbed/not transmitted by bone ***[1 mark]***.
So the parts of the plate behind bone remain white, as no X-ray radiation can reach them, while the rest turns black because it absorbs the X-ray radiation ***[1 mark]***.
b) If the human body is exposed to X-rays, it can cause cell damage ***[1 mark]***.

4 How to grade your answer:
Level 0: There is no relevant information. ***[No marks]***
Level 1: There is a brief description of how radio waves are created and received. The points made are basic and not linked together. ***[1-2 marks]***

Level 2: There is some description of how radio waves are produced from alternating current, transmitted, and received by conversion to charge oscillations. Some of the points made are linked together. ***[3-4 marks]***

Level 3: There is a clear and detailed explanation of how radio waves are produced from an alternating current, are transmitted through the air, and received by being converted into charge oscillations, producing the same alternating current as that which produced it. The points made are well-linked and the answer has a clear and logical structure. ***[5-6 marks]***

Here are some points your answer may include:
An alternating current (a current made of oscillating charges) flows through the walkie-talkie.
These charges oscillate in the walkie-talkie's aerial.
These oscillating charges produce radio waves with the same frequency as the oscillation of the charges.
These radio waves travel through the air to the second walkie-talkie.
When they reach the second walkie-talkie, they are absorbed by the walkie-talkie's aerial.
The energy carried by the radio waves is transferred to the charges in the receiver aerial.
This causes charges in the aerial to oscillate with the same frequency as the radio-wave.
This produces an alternating current in the second walkie-talkie identical to the one which created the radio waves.

Pages 188-189 — Absorbing and Emitting Radiation

1 a) It is constant ***[1 mark]***.
b) The amount of radiation being emitted by the object is more than the amount of being radiation absorbed by the object ***[1 mark]***.
2 a) A ***[1 mark]***
Star C is hotter than star A, so it must have a shorter peak wavelength than star A. Star B is cooler than star A, so it must have a longer peak wavelength than star A. Option A is the only one where this is the case.
b) Star B ***[1 mark]***. It has the lowest temperature, so its peak wavelength must be the longest ***[1 mark]***.
3 a) Some of the radiation that reaches the Earth's surface is absorbed and then re-emitted. ***[1 mark]***
b) At Time 1, radiation from the Sun hits point P, so the Earth at point P is absorbing radiation from the Sun ***[1 mark]***. The Earth at point P is absorbing more radiation than it is emitting, so the local temperature is increasing ***[1 mark]***. At Time 2, point P is facing away from the Sun and so the Earth at point P absorbs no radiation from the Sun ***[1 mark]***. The Earth is emitting more radiation than it is absorbing, so the local temperature is decreasing ***[1 mark]***.

Page 190 — The Greenhouse Effect

1 a) methane ***[1 mark]***
b) Any one from: e.g. burning fossil fuels ***[1 mark]***, produces CO_2 (a greenhouse gas) ***[1 mark]*** / deforestation ***[1 mark]***, reduces the number of trees which remove CO_2 (a greenhouse gas) from the atmosphere ***[1 mark]*** / agriculture ***[1 mark]***, farm animals produce methane (a greenhouse gas) ***[1 mark]*** / creating waste ***[1 mark]***, methane and CO_2 (greenhouse gases) are released into the atmosphere as waste decays ***[1 mark]***.
2 a) Some radiation emitted from the surface of the Earth is absorbed by carbon dioxide in the atmosphere ***[1 mark]***. Radiation is then re-emitted by the atmosphere in all directions, including towards the Earth, helping to keep it warmer than it would otherwise be ***[1 mark]***.
b) The graphs do show a positive correlation between atmospheric carbon dioxide and temperature ***[1 mark]*** — as one increases so does the other and vice versa, e.g. they both increase from about 25 000 years before the present up to today ***[1 mark]***. However, correlation does not prove cause like Isaac has said ***[1 mark]***. They could show correlation by chance, or be linked by a third variable ***[1 mark]***.

Chapter P2 — Sustainable Energy

Page 191 — Energy Stores and Transfers

Warm-up
1) gravitational potential
2) nuclear
3) elastic
4) chemical

1 a) thermal ***[1 mark]***
b) The work done by the electric current is equal to the energy transferred to the kettle ***[1 mark]***.
2 Energy is transferred mechanically ***[1 mark]*** from the gravitational potential energy stores of Sonja and the bike ***[1 mark]*** to the kinetic energy stores of Sonja and the bike ***[1 mark]***.

Page 192 — Conservation of Energy and Power

1 Some of the energy in the thermal energy store of the hot potato is dissipated to the thermal energy store of the room. ***[1 mark]***
2 a) Work done is the same as energy transferred.
time = 125 × 60 = 7500 seconds
power = energy transferred ÷ time so
energy transferred = power × time
= 600 × 7500 = 4 500 000 = 4500 kJ
So work done = **4500 kJ**
[4 marks for the correct answer, otherwise 1 mark for correct equation, 1 mark for the correct substitution and 1 mark for correct conversion to kJ.]
b) Time taken = 125 × 60 = 7500 seconds
power = energy transferred ÷ time
= 3 930 000 ÷ 7500 = **524 W**
[2 marks for correct answer, otherwise 1 mark for correct substitution.]
c) Convert W to kW:
400 ÷ 1000 = 0.4 kW
Time for one load in hours = 165 ÷ 60 = 2.75 hours
Number of weeks in a year = 52
So total time washing machine is used in one year = 2.75 × 52 = 143 hours
Then find total energy transferred by washing machine B in one year in kWh:
energy transferred = power × time
= 0.4 × 143
= 57.2 kWh
Convert price per kWh into pounds:
16 ÷ 100 = £0.16
Total cost = price per kWh × energy transferred in kWh
= 0.16 × 57.2
= £9.152
= **£9.15**
[4 marks for correct answer, otherwise 1 mark for converting W to kW, 1 mark for calculating the total time in hours and 1 mark for calculating the energy transferred in kWh.]

Chapter P2

Page 193 — Efficiency and Sankey Diagrams

1 a) Any one from: e.g. by heating the fan / by heating the surroundings / transferred away by sound waves *[1 mark]*.

b) E.g. Convert 2kJ to J = 2 × 1000 = 2000 J
Find the energy that is transferred usefully:
useful output energy = input energy – wasted energy
= 7500 – 2000 = 5500 J
Using the scale of 1 square width = 500 J:

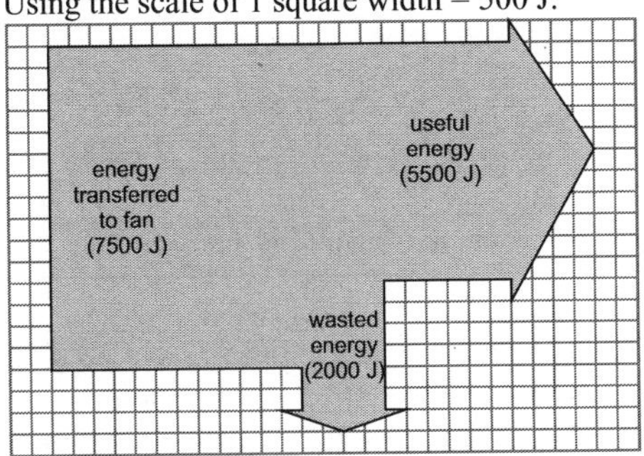

[1 mark for appropriate scale, 1 mark for the start of the diagram and the two arrows being the correct widths and 1 mark for correct labels.]

c) $\text{efficiency} = \frac{\text{useful energy transferred}}{\text{total energy transferred}}$

$= \frac{5500}{7500} = 0.73333... =$ **0.73 (to 2 s.f.)**

[2 marks for correct answer, otherwise 1 mark for calculating the efficiency and 1 mark for giving your answer to 2 s.f.]

2 $\text{efficiency} = \frac{\text{useful energy transferred}}{\text{total energy transferred}}$

so, useful energy transferred = efficiency × total energy transferred
= 0.76 × 2500 = 1900 J
So 1900 J of energy is transferred to the thermal energy store of the water each second.
418 000 J of energy is needed to boil the water.
So, time taken to boil water = 418 000 ÷ 1900 = **220 seconds**
[4 marks for the correct answer, otherwise 1 mark for rearranging efficiency equation, 1 mark for substitution into rearranged equation and 1 mark for division of total energy needed by energy transferred to the water per second.]

Pages 194-195 — Energy Resources

Warm-up
Renewable — biofuel, solar, tidal, hydroelectricity
Non-renewable — oil, coal, natural gas, nuclear fuel

1 a) Wind is a renewable energy resource *[1 mark]* because it will never run out *[1 mark]*.

b) The wind causes the blades of the wind turbine to rotate *[1 mark]*, which turns a generator inside, producing electricity *[1 mark]*.

2 The biofuels are burned in order to heat water *[1 mark]*. The water boils to form steam *[1 mark]*, which moves and turns a turbine *[1 mark]*. The turbine is connected to a generator, which spins a magnet near to a coil of wire, generating a potential difference across the wire *[1 mark]*. This causes a current to flow, which is electricity *[1 mark]*.

3 a) Fossil fuels are extracted at a fast enough rate that there is always some in stock, so they are reliable, as Stephen says *[1 mark]*. But some renewable energy resources can be unreliable, especially the ones that depend on the weather *[1 mark]*. Fossil fuels are slowly running out and they damage the environment when being used, which means they are not sustainable *[1 mark]*. Renewable energy resources will never run out and do comparatively little damage to the environment when being used, so they are sustainable, as Max says *[1 mark]*.

b) E.g. Both energy resources are reliable *[1 mark]*. Both methods of producing electricity have minimal running costs *[1 mark]* and no fuel costs *[1 mark]*. Hydroelectric power stations require the flooding of valleys, which causes a loss of habitat for animals/plants *[1 mark]*. Tidal barrages create no pollution, but they do alter the habitat of nearby animals *[1 mark]*.

Page 196 — Trends in Energy Use

1 a) 2015: 3.0 + 1.6 = 4.6 TWh
1995: 3.8 + 0.2 = 4.0 TWh
4.6 – 4.0 = **0.6 TWh**
[2 marks for a correct answer, otherwise 1 mark for correctly calculating the total amount of electricity produced in 1995 and 2015.]

b) How to grade your answer:

Level 0: There is no relevant information. ***[No marks]***

Level 1: There is a brief description of a trend shown by the graph. There is no data mentioned. The points made are basic and not linked together. ***[1-2 marks]***

Level 2: There is a description of at least one trend shown by the graph, and some explanation of the factors which may have influenced this trend. There is at least one piece of data used to illustrate the trends. Some of the points made are linked together. ***[3-4 marks]***

Level 3: There is a clear and detailed description of at least two trends shown by the graph, and explanation of several factors which may have influenced these trends. Data from the bar chart is used clearly to provide evidence for the trends described. The points made are well-linked and the answer has a clear and logical structure. ***[5-6 marks]***

Here are some points your answer may include:
From 1995 to 2015, the production of electricity on the whole has increased from 3.8 TWh to 4.6 TWh, because the demand for electricity within this small country is gradually increasing.
Energy demand could be increasing due to the population increasing, technological advances or changes in the population's lifestyles.
From 1995 to 2015, the production of electricity from non-renewable sources decreased from 3.8 to 3.0 TWh.
From 1995 to 2015 the production of electricity from renewable resources increased from 0.2 to 1.6 TWh.
This may be because the country is trying to decrease their reliance on non-renewable energy sources because they will run out one day, and renewable resources won't run out.
They could also be decreasing their non-renewable usage in order to decrease the environmental damage caused by using non-renewables.
If the non-renewable resource being used is nuclear fuel, they could be increasingly worried about nuclear accidents, and so want to cut down on their use of nuclear fuel.
The government may have introduced targets for using renewable energy resources in order to reduce the negative impact of using non-renewable sources.

You could have used any data from the graph, as long as it supported the trend you were describing.

Chapter P3

Pages 197-198 — The National Grid

Warm-up
From top to bottom:
alternating voltage, alternating voltage, direct voltage

1 a) 230 V, 50 Hz ***[1 mark]***
b) i) 230 V ***[1 mark]***
ii) 0 V ***[1 mark]***

2 From top to bottom:
false, true, true
[2 marks for all correct, otherwise 1 mark for 1 or 2 correct]

3 a) The man has an electric potential of 0 V ***[1 mark]*** and the wire has an electric potential (of 230 V) so a potential difference exists between them ***[1 mark]***. This causes a current to flow through the man ***[1 mark]***.
b) Although there is no current flowing when it is switched off, there is still an electric potential in the live wire inside the socket ***[1 mark]***. So there is a still a potential difference between the live wire and the man ***[1 mark]***.

Chapter P3 — Electric Circuits

Page 199 — Circuits — The Basics

Warm-up
Current is the rate of flow of electric charge around a circuit.
A current will flow around a circuit if the circuit is closed and there is a source of potential difference.

1 a) E.g.

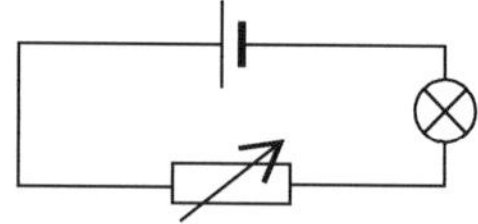

[1 mark for correct battery symbol, 1 mark for correct filament lamp symbol and 1 mark for all components connected by a single loop of wire.]

b) The potential difference remains the same ***[1 mark]*** and the current decreases ***[1 mark]***.

2 charge = current × time
Rearrange charge = current × time for current:
current = charge ÷ time
Convert time to seconds:
time = 3.0 × 60 × 60 = 10 800 s
current = 29 000 ÷ 10 800
= 2.68...
= **2.7 A (to 2 s.f.)**
[5 marks for correct answer, otherwise 1 mark for correctly recalling and rearranging the equation for current, 1 mark for converting time value into seconds, 1 mark for substituting in the correct values, 1 mark for calculating a value of 2.68... A and 1 mark for giving answer to 2 s.f.]

Page 200 — Resistance and V = I × R

1 potential difference = current × resistance
potential difference = 3.0 × 6.0 = **18 V**
[3 marks for correct answer, otherwise 1 mark for recalling the potential difference equation and 1 mark for substitution into the equation.]

2 a) She could have varied the length of the wire between the crocodile clips ***[1 mark]*** and divided the reading on the voltmeter by the reading on the ammeter to find the resistance for each length ***[1 mark]***.

b)

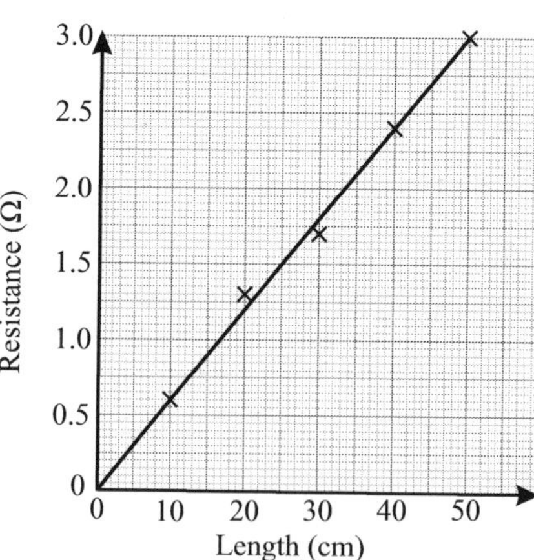

[1 mark for suitable scales, 1 mark for axes labelled with correct quantities and units, 1 mark for points plotted within half a square of their correct position and 1 mark for suitable line of best fit.]

c) E.g. **1.5 Ω** (accept any correct answer for your line of best fit) ***[1 mark]***.

Page 201 — Resistance and I-V Characteristics

1 a) B ***[1 mark]***
b) A linear component is a component with a constant resistance ***[1 mark]***. The *I-V* characteristic of a linear component is a straight line ***[1 mark]***.

2 How to grade your answer:
Level 0: There is no relevant information. ***[No marks]***
Level 1: There is a brief description of a method to measure how the resistance of the diode changes with current. There is little to no discussion of the validity of the results. ***[1 to 2 marks]***
Level 2: There is a description of a method to measure how the resistance of the diode changes with current. There is some discussion of the validity of the results. ***[3 to 4 marks]***
Level 3: There is a clear and detailed description of a method to measure how the resistance of the diode changes with current. The answer includes a good discussion of the validity of the results. ***[5 to 6 marks]***

Here are some points your answer may include:
James should change the resistance of the variable resistor in steps.
For each setting of the variable resistor, he should record the potential difference across the diode by reading the value off the voltmeter.
He should also record the current through the circuit by taking a reading off the ammeter.
In order for the results of the experiment to be valid, the results must be repeatable and reproducible.
To get a valid set of results, he should take repeated readings of current and potential difference for each setting of the variable resistor and calculate an average.
He should also turn off the circuit and allow it to cool down between readings, as if the circuit starts to heat up it could interfere with the repeatability and reproducibility of his results, and so affect their validity.
To see how resistance varies with current he could plot the average potential difference and current values on an *I-V* graph with a line of best fit.

Chapter P3

Page 202 — Circuit Devices

1 a)

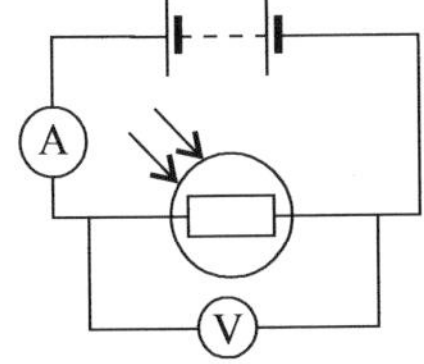

[1 mark for correct LDR symbol, 1 mark for LDR, ammeter and power supply in series and 1 mark for voltmeter in parallel across LDR.]

b) E.g. The resistance of the LDR increases as light intensity decreases ***[1 mark]***.

The greater the percentage of the LDR covered, the less light can reach the LDR, and so the lower the light intensity.

2 a) When the temperature is low, the resistance is high, so the current is small and the lamp is dim ***[1 mark]***. As the temperature increases, the resistance of the thermistor decreases ***[1 mark]***. This means the current in the circuit increases ***[1 mark]***, and so the lamp gets brighter ***[1 mark]***.

b) E.g. the circuit will not give Mark the actual temperature ***[1 mark]***.

Pages 203-204 — Energy and Power in Circuits

Warm-up

True, False, True

1 a) A measure of the rate at which energy is transferred to the component/how much energy is transferred to the component per second ***[1 mark]***.

b) Convert units to watts and seconds:
power = 0.015 × 1000 = 15 W
time = 10.0 × 60 × 60 = 36 000 s
energy transferred = power × time
= 15 × 36 000
= **540 000 J**

[4 marks for correct answer, otherwise 1 mark for correct conversion of units, 1 mark for recalling equation and 1 mark for correctly substituting the values into the equation.]

2 a) potential difference = work done ÷ charge, so
charge = work done ÷ potential difference
= $(2.76 \times 10^5) \div 230$ = **1200 C**

[3 marks for correct answer, otherwise 1 mark for rearranging work done equation for charge and 1 mark for correctly substituting in the values.]

b) energy transferred = charge × potential difference
= 980 × 230
= 225 400
= **225 kJ (to 3 s.f.)**

[4 marks for correct answer, otherwise 1 mark for correctly substituting in the values, 1 mark for correct unrounded answer, 1 mark for correctly rounding to 3 s.f. and 1 mark for correctly converting to kilojoules.]

3 a) power = potential difference × current
so current = power ÷ potential difference
= 75 ÷ 230 = 0.3260...
= **0.33 A (to 2 s.f.)**

[4 marks for the correct answer, otherwise 1 mark for rearranging the equation for current, 1 mark for substituting in the values, 1 mark for calculating a value of 0.3260... A and 1 mark for rounding to 2 s.f.]

b) E.g. energy is transferred from the mains supply electrically ***[1 mark]*** to the kinetic energy store of the motor ***[1 mark]***. This energy is transferred mechanically to the kinetic energy store of the blades ***[1 mark]***.

c) power = current^2 × resistance, so
resistance = $\frac{\text{power}}{\text{current}^2}$ = $2.45 \div 0.350^2$
= **20 W**

[3 marks for correct answer, otherwise 1 mark for rearranging the equation for resistance and 1 mark for substituting in the correct values.]

4 a) power = energy transferred ÷ time = 720 ÷ 76 = 9.4736... W
power = potential difference × current so
current = power ÷ potential difference
= 9.4736... ÷ 6.0 = 1.578...
= **1.6 A (to 2 s.f.)**

[5 marks for correct answer, otherwise 1 mark for recalling equations, 1 mark for calculating the power of the car for its slow speed setting, 1 mark for rearranging and correctly substituting into the equation for current, 1 mark for calculating a value of 1.578... A and 1 mark for correctly rounding to 2 s.f.]

b) The power of the car is higher ***[1 mark]***. So more energy is transferred away from the chemical energy store of the battery per second ***[1 mark]***.

Page 205 — Series and Parallel Circuits

1 A ***[1 mark]***

2 First calculate the equivalent resistance of the circuit:
equivalent resistance = 10.0 + 30.0 = 40.0 Ω
Then calculate the current in the circuit.
Rearrange potential difference = current × resistance for current, and calculate using the equivalent resistance:
current = potential difference ÷ resistance
= 3.00 ÷ 40.0
= 0.075 A
Calculate the potential difference across 30.0 Ω resistor using this value for current:
potential difference = current × resistance
= 0.075 × 30.0
= **2.25 V**

[5 marks for a correct answer, otherwise 1 mark for calculating the equivalent resistance, 1 mark for recalling the potential difference equation, 1 mark for calculating the current and 1 mark for substituting the correct values into the potential difference equation.]

3 How to grade your answer:

Level 0: There is no relevant information. ***[No marks]***

Level 1: There is a brief explanation about the effect of adding resistors in series or parallel. The points made are basic and not linked together. ***[1-2 marks]***

Level 2: There is an explanation for the effect of adding resistors in series and parallel. Some of the points made are linked together. ***[3-4 marks]***

Level 3: A logical and detailed explanation is given as to why adding resistors in series increases the total resistance, but adding them in parallel reduces it. The points made are well-linked and the answer has a clear and logical structure. ***[5-6 marks]***

Here are some points your answer may include:
In series, resistors share the potential difference from the power source.
The more resistors that are in series, the lower the potential difference across each one, and so the lower the current through each resistor (as $V = I \times R$).
Current is the same all round a series circuit, so adding a resistor will decrease the current for the whole circuit.
A decrease in total current means an increase in total resistance.
In parallel, all resistors have the same potential difference across them as the power source.

Chapter P3

Adding another resistor in parallel increases the current flowing in the circuit, as there are more paths for the current to flow through.
An increase in total current means a decrease in total resistance (because $V = I \times R$).

Page 206 — Investigating Series and Parallel Circuits

1 a) Find the equivalent resistance of the circuit:
potential difference = current × resistance so
resistance = potential difference ÷ current = 12 ÷ 0.25 = 48 Ω
This is the resistance of both bulbs, so divide by 2:
48 ÷ 2 = **24 Ω**
[3 marks for the correct answer, otherwise 1 mark for rearranging the equation for resistance and 1 mark for using this to correctly calculate the equivalent resistance of the circuit.]

b) i) First find the current through the circuit branch with bulb 3:
potential difference = current × resistance, so
current = potential difference ÷ resistance
= 12 ÷ 24 = 0.5 A
0.25 A is still flowing through the branch with bulbs 1 and 2.
Then find the current through the ammeter by adding the currents flowing through each branch:
current = 0.5 + 0.25 = **0.75 A**
[3 marks for correct answer, otherwise 1 mark for calculating the current for the branch with bulb 3 and 1 mark for stating the current in the branch with bulbs 1 and 2.]

The current flowing through the branch with bulbs 1 and 2 on it doesn't change when bulb 3 is added, as the resistance of this branch and the potential difference across it don't change.

ii) Bulb 3 is brighter because bulbs 1 and 2 have to share the source potential difference, while the potential difference across bulb 3 is the same as the source potential difference ***[1 mark]***. In addition, the current through the branch with bulbs 1 and 2 is lower than the current through the branch with bulb 3, as the branch with bulbs 1 and 2 has a higher resistance ***[1 mark]***.

c) i) The current through the ammeter decreases ***[1 mark]***.
ii) The brightness of bulbs 1 and 2 doesn't change ***[1 mark]***. Bulb 3 gets dimmer ***[1 mark]***.

Pages 207-208 — Permanent and Induced Magnets

Warm-up
T, F, T

1 a) Unlike poles attract each other. ***[1 mark]***
b) They are closer together where the magnetic field is stronger ***[1 mark]***.
c) A force is acting on both magnets due to their interacting magnetic fields ***[1 mark]***. The field lines are pointing away from the pole on each magnet, so the poles must both be of the same type (north) and so the force is repulsive ***[1 mark]***. So the two magnets will move away from each other ***[1 mark]***.

2 When a compass is far from other magnets, the north pole of a compass needle points towards the Earth's magnetic north pole (near the geographic north pole) ***[1 mark]***. This suggests that the Earth has a magnetic field ***[1 mark]*** and that the Earth's core is magnetic ***[1 mark]***.

3 a) N S N S

[1 mark for correctly labelled poles, 1 mark for the arrows pointing in the correct direction between the bars (N to S) and 1 mark for the arrows pointing in the correct direction (N to S) around each bar.]

b) While the permanent magnet was present, the magnetic material became an induced magnet, so had its own magnetic field ***[1 mark]***. When the permanent magnet was removed, the magnetic material demagnetised and lost its magnetic field ***[1 mark]***.

Pages 209-210 — Electromagnetism

1 a) The magnetic field around each loop of wire add together ***[1 mark]***. This causes the strength of the magnetic field to increase ***[1 mark]***.
b) If the current is stopped, there will no longer be a magnetic field around the solenoid ***[1 mark]***.
c) The strength increased ***[1 mark]***.
d) E.g. a permanent magnet always has a magnetic field, but an electromagnet can be turned on and off by turning an electric current on and off ***[1 mark]***.
e) E.g. place a compass near to the solenoid ***[1 mark]***. If a magnetic field is present, the compass needle will move to align itself with the magnetic field of the solenoid ***[1 mark]***.

2 a)

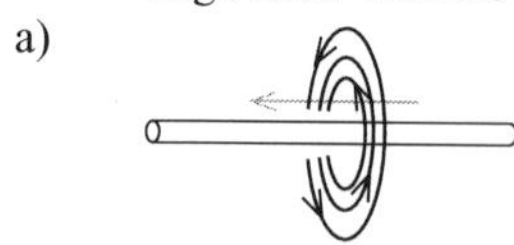

[1 mark for circular field lines with rod at the centre and lines getting further apart and 1 mark for arrows pointing in the direction shown.]

You can work this out using the right-hand thumb rule — point your right thumb in the direction of the current and your curled fingers will show the direction of the field lines. Bingo.

b) The direction of the field will also be reversed ***[1 mark]***.
c) E.g. increase the current ***[1 mark]***.

3 E.g. the electromagnetic effect led to lots of electromagnetic machines and devices, including the electromagnetic relay ***[1 mark]***. Electromagnetic relays were used to create telegraphs, which are used for communications ***[1 mark]***. Telegraphs allowed people to communicate across long distances much quicker than they had before ***[1 mark]***.

Page 211 — The Motor Effect

1 a)

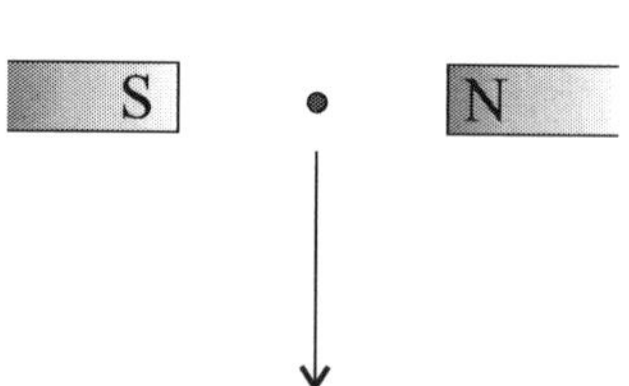

[1 mark for arrow pointing downwards]

b) The direction will be reversed ***[1 mark]*** but the size of the force will not change ***[1 mark]***.

2 a) Convert cm to m = 30.0 cm ÷ 100 = 0.3 m
force = magnetic flux density × current × length
= 2.2 × 15 × 0.3 = **9.9 N**
[3 marks for correct answer, otherwise 1 mark for the correct conversion and 1 mark for correctly substituting into the correct equation.]

b) The magnetic field around the wire and the magnetic field between the poles interact with each other, resulting in a force on the wire ***[1 mark]***.

Page 212 — Electric Motors

1 a) i) A current flows in different directions through each side of the coil (both of which are perpendicular to the magnetic field) ***[1 mark]***. Each side of the coil experience forces in opposite directions ***[1 mark]***, which causes the coil to rotate ***[1 mark]***.

Chapter P4

ii) Any one from: swap the polarity of the d.c. supply (reverse the current) ***[1 mark]*** / swap the magnetic poles over (reverse the field) ***[1 mark]***.

b) The size of the current through the coil ***[1 mark]***.
The magnetic flux density/strength of the magnetic field ***[1 mark]***.

c) E.g. motors that drive conveyor belts in factories ***[1 mark]***. They make the job easier by reducing the physical human effort needed to move products / they make the job quicker as they can move products faster than a human could ***[1 mark]***.

Page 213 — Transformers

1 a) Power is the rate of energy transfer, so due to conservation of energy between the two coils, the input power must equal the output power ***[1 mark]***. Power is given by the equation power = potential difference × current ***[1 mark]***. So if the potential difference across the secondary coil is higher than across the primary coil, the current in the secondary coil must be lower than in the primary coil to keep the value of output power equal to the input power ***[1 mark]***.

b) $V_p \times I_p = V_s \times I_s$ so $I_s = (V_p \times I_p) \div V_s$
$I_s = (30.0 \times 20.0) \div 40.0 =$ **15 A**
[3 marks for correct answer, otherwise 1 mark for correct rearrangement and 1 mark for correct substitution.]

2 Transformers are used to increase the potential difference of the generated electricity before transmission ***[1 mark]***. The transformer keeps the power of the electricity constant, so increasing the potential difference decreases the current (as power = potential difference × current) ***[1 mark]***. The higher the electric current, the more energy is wasted due to heating in the cables ***[1 mark]***. So transmitting the electricity at a lower current reduces the energy lost, making the national grid more efficient at transferring energy ***[1 mark]***.

Chapter P4 — Explaining Motion

Page 214 — Forces and Newton's Third Law

Warm-up
When two objects interact, they exert equal and opposite forces on each other.

1 a) As Dave pushes the wall, the wall will exert an equal and opposite force on Dave ***[1 mark]***. As there is no friction, Dave will have a resultant force pushing him away from the wall which causes him to move ***[1 mark]***.

b) Contact force: e.g. normal contact force ***[1 mark]***
Non-contact force: e.g. weight ***[1 mark]***

2 $R_T = R_P$ as the two forces are an equal and opposite pair from Newton's Third Law ***[1 mark]***. $R_P = W_P$ as the plate is in equilibrium ***[1 mark]***. $W_P = W_E$ as the two forces are an equal and opposite pair from Newton's Third Law ***[1 mark]***. Therefore $W_E = R_T$ ***[1 mark]***.

Page 215 — Mass and Weight

Warm-up
False, True, True

1 a) Weight is the downwards force that acts on an object due to gravitational attraction ***[1 mark]***.

b) weight = mass of object × gravitational field strength
= 65 × 10 = **650 N**
[3 marks for correct answer, otherwise 1 mark for recalling equation and 1 mark for substituting in the correct numbers.]

c) Rearrange weight = mass × gravitational field strength for gravitational field strength:
gravitational field strength = weight ÷ mass
= 232 ÷ (65 + 80)
= **1.6 N/kg**
[4 marks for correct answer, otherwise 1 mark for rearranging weight equation for gravitational field strength, 1 mark for substitution of correct values, 1 mark for the correct numerical value, 1 mark for the correct unit.]

Page 216 — Scalars and Vectors

Warm-up
Scalar — distance, speed
Vector — displacement, velocity, force

1 a) 7 m ***[1 mark]***
To find the distance, simply measure the distance from A to B on the diagram with a ruler. Then convert your measurement to metres using the scale: 1 cm = 1 m.

b) 7 m + 5 m = 12 m ***[1 mark]***

c) A ——→ C .... B
[1 mark for arrow of correct length in the correct direction.]

d) 2 m ***[1 mark]***

2 C ***[1 mark]***

Page 217 — Calculating Speed

1 a) average speed = distance ÷ time ***[1 mark]***

b) 22 minutes = 22 × 60 = 1320 s
average speed = distance ÷ time, so
distance = average speed × time
= 4.0 × 1320 = 5280 m
5280 m = 5280 ÷ 1000 = 5.28 km = **5.3 km (to 2 s.f.)**
[4 marks for correct answer to two significant figures, otherwise 1 mark for correctly converting the time into seconds, 1 mark for correctly substituting the numbers into the rearranged equation, 1 mark for correct numerical answer for distance travelled.]

2 a) Typical walking speed = 1.4 m/s (accept 1-2 m/s)
average speed = distance ÷ time , so
time = distance ÷ average speed
= 2800 ÷ 1.4 = 2000 s
Convert 2000 s to hours:
2000 ÷ (60 × 60) = 0.555... = **0.6 hours (to 1 s.f.)**
So, Cecil's expectation is not sensible (as it will take him much less than an hour and a half to walk to work).
[5 marks for correct answer and conclusion, otherwise 1 mark for using a suitable estimate for walking speed, 1 mark for stating the correct equation, 1 mark for calculating the time taken and 1 mark for giving the time taken to 1 s.f.]
Don't worry if your answer for the time taken is not quite the same as this one. As long as you've used a sensible value for the typical walking speed, and given your answer to 1 significant figure, you'll get the marks.

b) time = 15 × 60 = 900 s, 7.2 km = 7200 m
average speed = distance ÷ time = 7200 ÷ 900 = **8 m/s**
[3 marks for correct answer, otherwise 1 mark for correctly converting the time into seconds and km into m, 1 mark for correctly substituting the numbers into the equation.]

Page 218 — Acceleration

1 a) acceleration = change in speed ÷ time taken
= 3.2 ÷ 8.0 = **0.4 m/s²**
[4 marks for the correct answer, otherwise 1 mark for recalling the equation for acceleration, 1 mark for substituting the values into the correct equation, 1 mark for correct value and 1 mark for correct unit.]

Chapter P4

b) Rearrange acceleration = change in speed ÷ time taken, so:
change in speed = acceleration × time taken
= 0.4 × 6.0 = 2.4 m/s
change in speed = final speed – initial speed, so:
final speed = change in speed + initial speed
= 2.4 + 3.2 = **5.6 m/s**
[3 marks for correct answer, otherwise 1 mark for rearranging acceleration equation and 1 mark for calculating the change in speed.]

You can still get the marks if you carried over an incorrect value from a).

c) Trigger's speed is constant, but her velocity is changing. ***[1 mark]***

She is constantly changing direction, so velocity is changing, even though the value stays the same.

2 1.2×10^3 m = 1200 m
$(\text{final speed})^2 - (\text{initial speed})^2 = 2 \times \text{acceleration} \times \text{distance}$
Rearrange for final speed:
final speed
$= \sqrt{(2 \times \text{acceleration} \times \text{distance}) + (\text{initial speed})^2}$
$= \sqrt{(2 \times 0.25 \times 1200) + (5.0)^2} = 25$ m/s
change in speed = final speed – initial speed
= 25 – 5.0 = 20 m/s
Rearrange acceleration = change in speed ÷ time taken:
time taken = change in speed ÷ acceleration
= 20 ÷ 0.25 = **80 s**
[5 marks for the correct answer, otherwise 1 mark for rearranging equation for final speed, 1 mark for calculating final speed, 1 mark for calculating the change in speed, and 1 mark for substituting the values into the rearranged acceleration equation.]

Page 219 — Investigating Motion

1 a) How to grade your answer:

Level 0: There is no relevant information. ***[No marks]***

Level 1: There is a brief explanation of the experiment, with no description of how to calculate the acceleration. The points made are basic and not linked together. ***[1 to 2 marks]***

Level 2: There is an explanation of how the experiment is carried out, and how to calculate the acceleration. Some of the points made are linked together. ***[3 to 4 marks]***

Level 3: There is a detailed explanation of how the experiment is carried out, including details on how to calculate the acceleration from the results. The points made are well-linked and the answer has a clear and logical structure. ***[5 to 6 marks]***

Here are some points your answer may include:
Alice should measure and record the distance between light gates B and C.
Alice should release the trolley from rest from a marked position just before light gate A.
The time at which it passes through light gates A, B and C should be recorded.
The acceleration can be found using:
acceleration = change in speed ÷ time taken
(ignoring friction).
Since the trolley started at rest at point A, the initial speed is 0 m/s.
So the change in speed is equal to the average speed of the trolley on the runway.
The average speed on the runway can be calculated using the time difference between the time values at light gates B and C, the distance between B and C, and the equation average speed = distance ÷ time.
The time spent accelerating can be found by calculating the difference between the two time values at light gates A and B.
Calculate the acceleration on the ramp by substituting these values into the equation.
To improve the accuracy, Alice could repeat the experiment at least three times, keeping all variables the same, e.g. same trolley, starting from the same marked place.
Alice can then calculate an average acceleration value.

Alice could also use the light gates to measure the speed of the trolley directly at each light gate, in which case you wouldn't need light gate C.

b) Using a stopwatch introduces human error due to reaction times ***[1 mark]***.

c) It would increase ***[1 mark]***.

A greater angle will give a greater acceleration on the ramp, which will give a greater speed on the runway.

d) It would decrease ***[1 mark]***.

The more friction there is between the trolley and the ramp, the lower the acceleration of the trolley on the ramp, and so the lower its speed on the runway.

Pages 220-221 — Distance-Time Graphs

1 a)

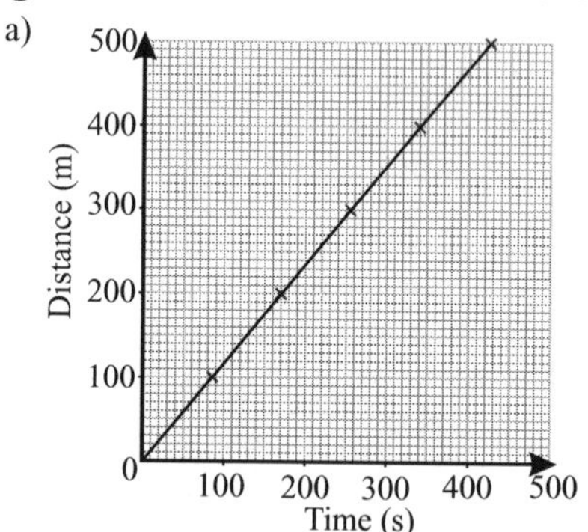

[3 marks for graph plotted correctly, otherwise 1 mark for three points correct, 1 mark for a straight line going through all plotted points]

b) 350 m (accept between 345 m and 355 m) ***[1 mark]***

c) 215 s (accept between 210 s and 220 s) ***[1 mark]***

d) E.g. referring to the same point on the boat / making sure that the timings are measured from exactly level with the posts / making sure timings are made close to the posts to avoid parallax ***[1 mark for any correct answer]***

2 a) She accelerates for 7.5 minutes ***[1 mark]*** before travelling at a steady speed for 2.5 minutes ***[1 mark]***.

b) Distance travelled in m = 4 × 1000 = 4000 m
Time taken in s = 25 × 60 = 1500 s
speed = distance ÷ time = 4000 ÷ 1500
= 2.66... = **2.7 m/s (to 2 s.f.)**
[4 marks for the correct answer, otherwise 1 mark for converting 4 km into m and 25 mins into s, 1 mark for using the correct speed equation, 1 mark for substituting in the correct values and 1 mark for giving the answer to 2 s.f.]

3 a) Speed = gradient = (92 – 20) ÷ (6 – 3) = 72 ÷ 3 = **24 m/s**
(accept between 23 m/s and 25 m/s)
[3 marks for correct answer, otherwise 1 mark for stating that speed = gradient, 1 mark for a correct calculation attempting to find the gradient of the straight part of the distance-time graph between 3 and 6 seconds.]

Chapter P4

b)

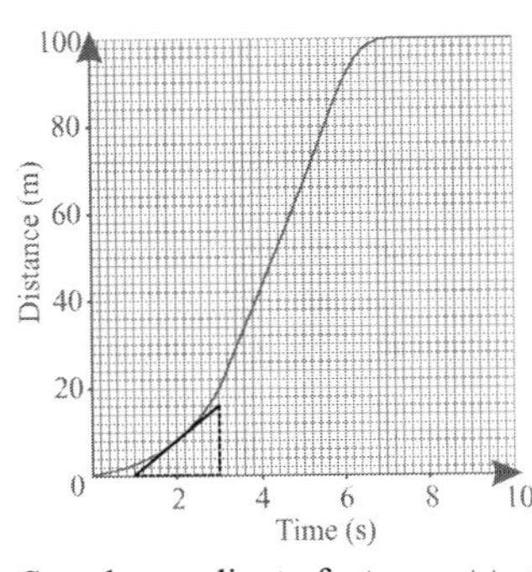

Speed = gradient of a tangent to the line
= (16 – 0) ÷ (3 – 1) = 16 ÷ 2 = **8 m/s**
(accept between 6 m/s and 10 m/s)
[3 marks for correct answer, otherwise 1 mark for a correct tangent to the line at 2 s, 1 mark for a correct calculation of the gradient of the tangent drawn.]

Pages 222-223 — Velocity-Time Graphs

Warm-up
A: constant deceleration, B: steady velocity
1 distance ***[1 mark]***
2 C ***[1 mark]***
3 a)

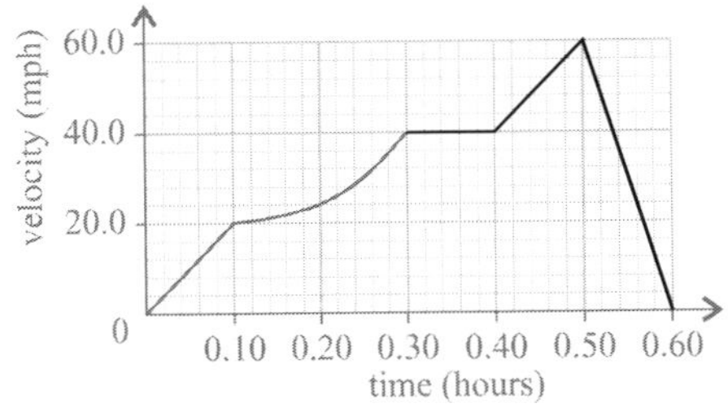

[1 mark for a flat line between 0.30 and 0.40 hours at 40 mph, 1 mark for straight line slope from 0.40 and 0.50 hours from 40 mph to 60 mph, 1 mark for straight line slope between 0.50 hours and 0.60 hours from 60 mph to 0 mph.]

b) Each small square represents:
0.02 hours × 4 mph = 0.08 miles
Number of squares under the graph between 0 and 0.30 hours = 78
Distance travelled = 0.08 × 78 = **6.24 miles**
(accept between 6 and 6.4 miles)
[3 marks for the correct answer, otherwise 1 mark for finding the value of 1 small square, 1 mark for counting the squares under the graph between 0 and 0.30 hours.]

c) Draw a tangent to the curve at 0.20 hours, e.g.

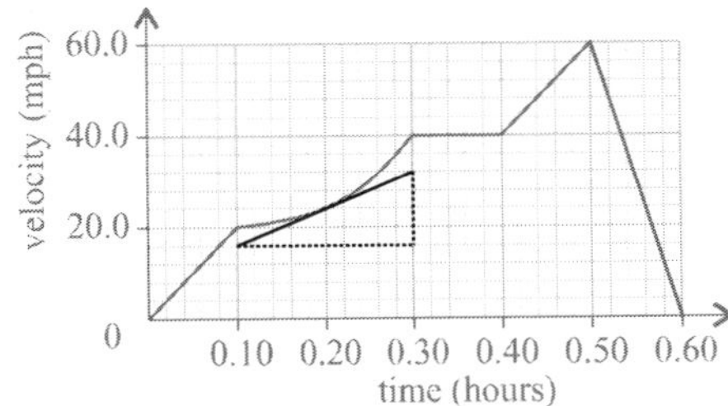

acceleration = gradient
change in velocity = 32 – 16 = 16 mph
16 mph in m/s: 16 × 1600 = 25 600 metres per hour
25 600 ÷ 3600 = 7.11... m/s
change in time = 0.30 – 0.10 = 0.20 hours
0.20 hours in s: 0.20 × 3600 = 720 s
gradient = change in velocity ÷ change in time
= 7.11... ÷ 720 = 0.009876...
= **0.0099 m/s² (to 2 s.f.)**
(accept between 0.0097 and 0.0101)
[5 marks for correct answer, otherwise 1 mark for drawing a tangent to the curve at 0.20 hours, 1 mark for converting all values to metres and seconds, 1 mark for using the correct equation for calculating the gradient and 1 mark for giving the answer to 2 s.f.]

Page 224 — Free Body Diagrams and Forces

1 a) 10 000 N to the right ***[1 mark]***
The forces acting up and down are equal and act in opposite directions, so cancel each other out. The forces acting left and right combine to make a resultant force of 10 000 N to the right.

b) A resultant force is the sum of all the individual forces acting on an object ***[1 mark]*** taking their directions into account ***[1 mark]***.

c) Upwards force = normal contact force ***[1 mark]***
Downwards force = weight ***[1 mark]***

2 Friction = 60 – 40 = 20 N
Normal contact force = weight = 50 N

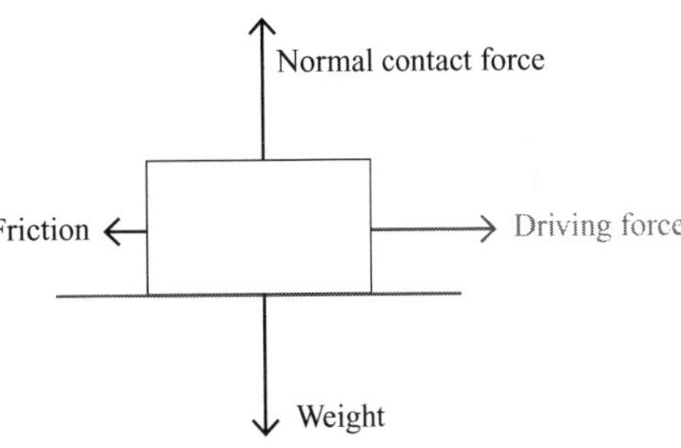

[1 mark for drawing an arrow 1 cm long pointing to the left, 1 mark for a 2.5 cm long arrow pointing upwards, 1 mark for a 2.5 cm long arrow pointing downwards and 1 mark for correctly labelling the forces.]

Pages 225-226 — Forces and Scale Drawings

1 All the forces acting on the object are balanced. ***[1 mark]***
2 D ***[1 mark]***
3 Draw a scale drawing with a sensible scale, e.g. 1 square = 100 N:

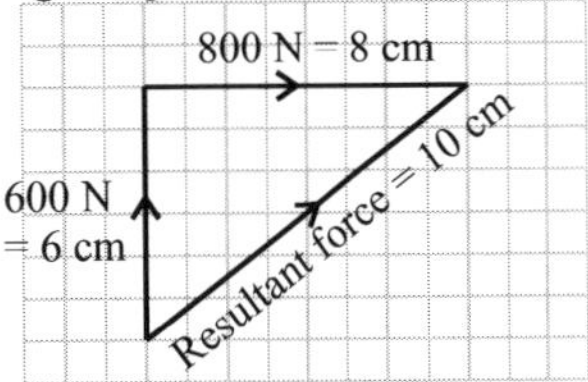

Measure the longest side: Length = 10 cm
And, using the scale suggested, 10 × 100 = **1000 N**
[3 marks for correct answer, otherwise 1 mark for drawing a scale drawing and 1 mark for choosing a sensible scale.]

Chapter P4

4 a)

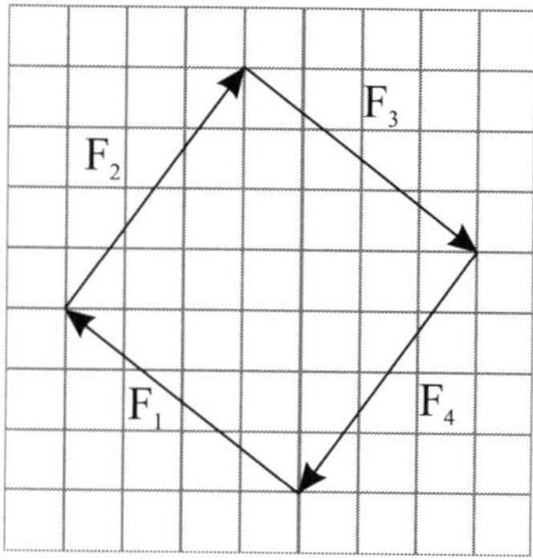

[1 mark for arrows of correct length, 1 mark for all arrows drawn tip-to-tail, 1 mark for arrow drawn to form closed shape]

b) E.g.

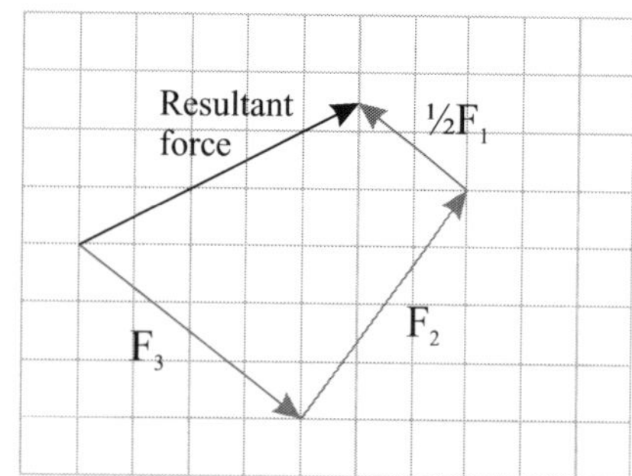

[1 mark for given arrows drawn to scale, tip-to-tail, 1 mark for resultant force arrow drawn correctly]

Arrow length = 2.8 cm (accept any value between 2.7 cm and 2.9 cm or equivalent on appropriate scale) *[1 mark]*

Force = 2.8 × 20 = **56 N**

(accept any value between 54 N and 58 N) *[1 mark]*

Page 227 — Newton's First Law and Circular Motion

Warm-up

Newton's First Law of motion says that an object will remain stationary or moving at a constant velocity if the resultant force acting on it is zero. If the resultant force acting is non-zero, it will accelerate.

1 The rocket will increase in speed *[1 mark]*, and change direction *[1 mark]*.

2 Carlos is correct because the force acting on the ball is always perpendicular to the motion of the ball *[1 mark]* so it does not change its speed, only its direction *[1 mark]*. Since the ball's direction is always changing, its velocity is always changing (even though its speed remains the same) *[1 mark]*.

Pages 228-229 — Momentum and Newton's Second Law

1 Rearrange formula: momentum = mass × velocity, so mass = momentum ÷ velocity
= 46 000 ÷ 15 = 3066.6... = **3100 kg (to 2 s.f.)**

[4 marks for the correct answer, otherwise 1 mark for recalling and rearranging the momentum equation, 1 mark for substituting the values into the rearranged formula, 1 mark for the correct value and 1 mark for giving the answer to 2 s.f.]

2 B *[1 mark]*

As momentum = mass × velocity, halving the mass and doubling the velocity will mean the magnitude of the momentum doesn't change. Momentum is a vector, so a change in direction means the momentum will change from positive to negative (assuming north is the positive direction).

3 In the left diagram, the total momentum of the system is equal to the mass of the moving ball multiplied by its velocity *[1 mark]*. As it hits the line of balls, it transfers this momentum to them and comes to a stop. All of this momentum is transferred along the line of balls to the ball at the end of the line, which is why the middle balls don't move *[1 mark]*. This final ball has the momentum of the first ball, causing it to move with the same velocity (because all of the balls have the same mass) that the moving ball in the left diagram had *[1 mark]*. In the right diagram, the total momentum of the system is equal to the total momentum in left diagram *[1 mark]*.

4 momentum before = $(m_R \times v_R) + (m_B \times v_B)$
$= (m_R \times 0) + (4.5 \times 10^{-1} \times 3.0)$
$= 1.35$ kg m/s

momentum after = $(m_R + m_B) \times v_C$

momentum before = momentum after

So $(m_R + m_B) \times v_C = 1.35$

Rearrange for m_R:

$m_R = (1.35 \div v_C) - m_B$
$= (1.35 \div 2.5) - (4.5 \times 10^{-1}) =$ **0.09 kg**

[5 marks for correct answer, otherwise 1 mark for the correct momentum equations, 1 mark for calculating the momentum before, 1 mark for equating momentum before to momentum after, and 1 mark for rearranging for m_R.]

5 Find the change of momentum due to friction:

momentum before collision = momentum immediately after collision

momentum before collision = $(m_A \times v_A) + (m_B \times v_B)$
$= (2.0 \times 1.7) + (3.0 \times 1.2)$
$= 7$ kg m/s

so momentum 0 s after collision = 7 kg m/s

momentum 3.0 s after collision = $(m_{A+B} \times v_{A+B})$
$= (5.0 \times 0.50)$
$= 2.5$ kg m/s

so change in momentum due to friction = 7 – 2.5
= 4.5 kg m/s

change of momentum = resultant force × time for which it acts

so resultant force = change of momentum ÷ time for which it acts

so frictional force = 4.5 ÷ 3 = **1.5 N**

[6 marks for correct answer, otherwise 1 mark for recall of force = change in momentum ÷ time, 1 mark for calculation of total momentum before collision, 1 mark for statement of conservation of momentum, 1 mark for calculation of momentum after 3 seconds, 1 mark for calculation of change of momentum, and 1 mark for substitution into the force equation.]

You could have calculated the frictional force another way and still get the marks, e.g. use F = ma, and acceleration = change in velocity ÷ time.

Page 230 — Newton's Second Law and Inertia

1 a) E.g. a measure of how difficult it is to change the velocity of an object / ratio of force over acceleration / $m = F \div a$ *[1 mark for any correct definition]*

b) Trolley B has the highest inertial mass *[1 mark]*, because it has the lowest velocity after the force has been applied, so its velocity is more difficult to change (than the velocities of the other trolleys) *[1 mark]*.

2 a) Change force from mN to N: 0.5 mN ÷ 1000 = 0.0005 N

rearrange force = mass × acceleration, so

$$\text{mass} = \frac{\text{force}}{\text{acceleration}} = \frac{0.0005}{0.0025} = \mathbf{0.2\ kg}$$

[3 marks for correct answer, otherwise 1 mark for correct conversion and 1 mark for substituting the values into the rearranged equation.]

Chapter P4

b) B *[1 mark]*

The change in momentum is equal to final momentum – initial momentum, where momentum = mass × velocity. This is the same for both balls as they have the same mass and the same initial and final velocities. The time taken for the balls to come to a complete stop can be found from resultant force = change in momentum ÷ time. The resultant force acting on ball B is half that acting on ball A, so the time taken for ball B to stop must be double that of ball A.

Page 231 — Reaction Times

1 a) Hold a ruler between the open forefinger and thumb of the person being tested ***[1 mark]***. Align their finger to the zero line of the ruler, then drop the ruler without warning ***[1 mark]*** and have the test subject close their thumb and finger to catch the ruler ***[1 mark]***. The distance the ruler falls can be read from the ruler ***[1 mark]***. The time taken for it to fall can be calculated, as the acceleration (due to gravity) is constant. This is the reaction time of the test subject ***[1 mark]***.

b) Student A: (7.0 + 7.1 + 6.9) ÷ 3 = **7.0 cm** ***[1 mark]***
Student B: (8.3 × 3) – 8.4 – 8.3 = **8.2 cm** ***[1 mark]***

c) Student A, because the average distance fallen by the ruler was less for Student A than Student B ***[1 mark]***.

2 (final speed)^2 – (initial speed)^2 = 2 × acceleration × distance
(final speed)^2 = 0 + (2 × 10 × 0.45) = 9
final speed = 3 m/s
acceleration = change in speed ÷ time taken,
so time taken = change in speed ÷ acceleration
= 3 ÷ 10 = **0.3 s**
[4 marks for the correct answer, otherwise 1 mark for calculation of final speed, 1 mark for rearrangement of acceleration equation and 1 mark for substitution into rearranged equation.]

Page 232 — Stopping Distances and Vehicle Safety

Warm-up

The stopping distance of a vehicle is made up of the reaction distance and the braking distance. The braking distance of a car is longer if the car is heavily loaded and if conditions are icy. A vehicle is more likely to skid in wet conditions if its tyres are bald.

1 a) Stopping distance = reaction distance + braking distance
12 + 24 = **36 m** ***[1 mark]***

b) Any one from: e.g. the initial speed of the car is higher / the driver is (more) tired / the driver is influenced by drugs / the driver is influenced by alcohol ***[1 mark]***.

2 a) When an impact occurs, the foam is compressed and extends the time over which it takes for the cyclist's head to come to a stop ***[1 mark]***. The force needed to cause a change in momentum is related to the size of the change of momentum and the time over which the force acts ***[1 mark]***. Increasing the time taken for a given change of momentum decreases the force exerted, helping to prevent injury ***[1 mark]***.

b) Any two of: e.g. crumple zones, air bags, seat belts ***[1 mark for each correct answer]***.

Page 233 — Work Done and Energy Transfers

Warm-up

If a force does work on a stationary object, it may cause it to move. Energy is transferred to its kinetic energy store. If there is no friction or air resistance acting on the object, then the energy transferred will be equal to the work done.

1 75 000 Nm ***[1 mark]***

2 a) work done = force × distance = 21.0 × 35.0 = **735 J**
[3 marks for correct answer, otherwise 1 mark for recalling the equation for work done and 1 mark for substituting the values into the equation.]

b) The work done on the box as it slides across the ice is transferred to its kinetic energy store. When the box slides across the path, the energy transferred from its kinetic energy store is equal to the work done against friction.
So work done on box across ice = work done by box against friction on path.
Rearrange work done = force × distance for distance:
distance = work done ÷ force = 735 ÷ 17.5 = **42 m**
[3 marks for correct answer, otherwise 1 mark for rearranging work done equation for distance and 1 mark for using 735 J as the value of work done.]

You can still get the marks if you carried over an incorrect value from a).

Page 234 — Kinetic and Potential Energy Stores

1 gravitational potential energy = mass × gravitational field strength × height
= 65 × 10 × 10 = **6500 J**
[3 marks for correct answer, otherwise 1 mark for recalling the equation for gravitational potential energy and 1 mark substituting the values into the equation.]

2 a) B ***[1 mark]***

Use the equation KE = ½mv^2 to find the energy in the kinetic energy store of each car.

b) kinetic energy = ½ × mass × (speed)^2 = ½ × 1500 × 11^2
= 90 750 J
Assuming no friction or air resistance, energy in kinetic energy store at the bottom of the hill = energy in gravitational potential energy store at the when parked on the hill.
Rearrange potential energy = mass × height × gravitational field strength for height:
height = gravitational potential energy ÷ (mass × gravitational field strength)
= 90 750 ÷ (1500 × 10)
= 6.05 m = **6.1 m (to 2 s.f.)**
[5 marks for correct answer, otherwise 1 mark for calculating the energy in the kinetic energy store of the car, 1 mark for equating the energy in the kinetic and gravitational potential energy stores, 1 mark for substituting the values into the rearranged equation for gravitational potential energy, and 1 mark for rounding answer to 2 s.f.]

Page 235 — Energy Transfers and Power

1 It transfers 60 J of energy every second. ***[1 mark]***

2 The golf club has energy in its kinetic energy store ***[1 mark]***. Some of this energy is transferred mechanically to the kinetic energy store of the ball ***[1 mark]***. Some is transferred mechanically to the thermal energy stores of the golf club and the ball (and to the surroundings by heating) ***[1 mark]***. The rest is carried away by sound ***[1 mark]***.

3 a) It will decrease the time ***[1 mark]*** because more energy is being transferred to the kinetic energy store of the car per second ***[1 mark]*** so the car speeds up more quickly ***[1 mark]***.

b) The same amount of energy is needed to accelerate the car with both engines. The energy transferred by the old engine:
power = energy transferred ÷ time, so
energy transferred = power × time
= 32 000 × 9.0 = 288 000 J
The time taken for the new engine to transfer the same amount of energy is:
time = energy transferred ÷ power
= 288 000 ÷ 64 000
= **4.5 s**
[4 marks for correct answer, otherwise 1 mark for calculating the energy transferred, 1 mark for substituting into the rearranged equation and 1 mark for calculating the time.]

Chapter P5

Chapter P5 — Radioactive Materials

Page 236 — Developing the Model of the Atom

Warm-up

1×10^{-10} m

1 a) Thomson discovered electrons ***[1 mark]***. These can be removed from the atom proving that the atom can be split up ***[1 mark]***.

b) Atoms were thought of as a sphere of positive charge, with negatively charged electrons spread throughout it ***[1 mark]***.

c) He suggested the electrons could only orbit the nucleus at certain distances ***[1 mark]***.

2 Most of the alpha particles fired at the thin gold foil passed straight through undeflected ***[1 mark]*** but some were deflected by a large amount (a few even back the way they had come) ***[1 mark]***. This indicated that the atom is mostly made up of empty space / most of the atom's mass is concentrated at the centre in a tiny nucleus ***[1 mark]*** and the nucleus must be positively charged to repel the alpha particles ***[1 mark]***.

Page 237 — Isotopes and Radioactive Decay

Warm-up

mass number → A, atomic number → Z, $^{A}_{Z}X$ ← chemical symbol

1 a) Two neutrons and two protons ***[1 mark]***.

b) Gamma (γ) ray/radiation ***[1 mark]***

2 a) Atom A and atom B both contain the same number of protons, so first calculate the number of protons in atom A:

number of protons = mass number – number of neutrons
= 16 – 8
= 8 protons

Then calculate the mass number of atom B:

mass number = number of protons + number of neutrons
= 8 + 9 = **17**

[2 marks for the correct answer, otherwise 1 mark for calculating the number of protons in atom A.]

b) The neon isotope contains 10 protons, which is more than atom A ***[1 mark]***. So the charge on the neon isotope's nucleus is higher than the charge on atom A's nucleus ***[1 mark]***.

Page 238 — Penetration Properties and Decay Equations

1 a) It increases the positive charge on the nucleus / makes the nucleus 'more positive' ***[1 mark]***.

b) No effect ***[1 mark]***

2 a) The mass number decreases by 4 ***[1 mark]*** and the charge decreases by 2 ***[1 mark]***.

You can tell source A is emitting alpha radiation because the count rate drops significantly when paper is put between the source and the radiation detector, and only alpha radiation is stopped by paper.

b) $^{14}_{6}C \rightarrow ^{14}_{7}N + ^{0}_{-1}e$

[1 mark for the correct mass and atomic numbers for C, 1 mark for the correct mass and atomic numbers for N, 1 mark for knowing it's beta decay (correct symbol) and 1 mark for the correct values for the beta particle.]

You could also use the symbol b for the beta particle and still get the mark.

c) Source B ***[1 mark]***.

Pages 239-240 — Activity and Half-life

1 a) E.g. the time taken for the activity of a sample to halve ***[1 mark]***.

b) 75 seconds ***[1 mark]***

The initial activity is 60 cps. Half of this is 30 cps, which corresponds to 75 seconds on the time axis.

c) After 1 half-life, there will be 800 ÷ 2 = 400 undecayed nuclei remaining. After 2 half-lives, there will be 400 ÷ 2 = 200 undecayed nuclei remaining.
So 800 – 200 = **600** nuclei will have decayed.

[2 marks for correct answer, otherwise 1 mark for calculating the number of decayed/undecayed nuclei after one half-life]

d) After 2 half-lives, there are 200 undecayed nuclei.
The fraction is $\frac{200}{800}$, which simplifies to $\frac{1}{4}$ ***[1 mark]***

You don't even need the numbers to work out this ratio. For any radioactive isotope, after two half lives, the initial number of undecayed nuclei will have halved and then halved again. It will be one quarter of the original number, so the ratio is always 1:4.

2 Isotope 1, because more nuclei will decay per second ***[1 mark]***.

3 a)

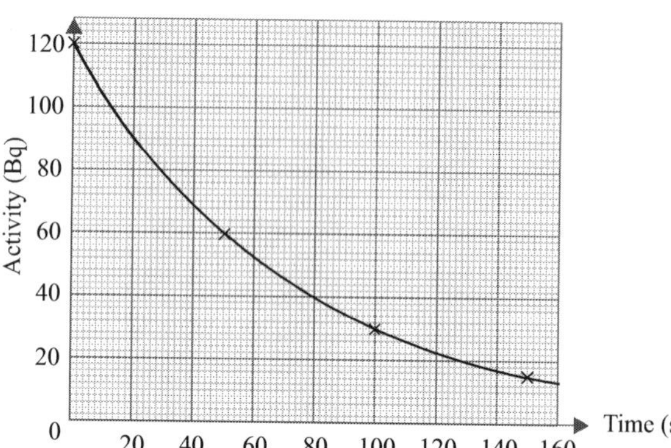

[3 marks in total — 2 marks for all points plotted correctly, otherwise 1 mark for three points plotted correctly and 1 mark for a smooth curve.]

Start the graph at 120 Bq. After 50 s, this will have halved to 60 Bq. After another 50 s (i.e. 100 s altogether), it will have halved again, to 30 Bq. Plot these points, then join them up with a nice smooth curve.

b) 70 Bq (accept between 68 Bq and 72 Bq)

[1 mark for correct value from your graph]

4 a) It takes a total of 2 hours and 30 minutes for the activity to halve from 8800 Bq to 4400 Bq,
so its half-life = (2 × 60) + 30 = **150 minutes**

[2 marks for the correct answer, otherwise 1 mark for finding the half-life in hours and minutes.]

b) Check how many half-lives pass during 6 hours and 15 minutes:
6 hours and 15 minutes = (6 × 60) + 15 = 375 minutes
375 ÷ 150 = 2.5 half-lives
The activity can only be worked out if a whole number of half-lives have passed, so calculate how many half-lives have passed from the time when activity = 6222 Bq:
1 hour 15 minutes = 60 + 15 = 75 minutes
375 – 75 = 300 minutes
300 ÷ 150 = 2 half-lives.
So now you can calculate the activity after 2 half-lives, with an initial activity of 6222 Bq:
After 1 half-life, the activity will be 6222 ÷ 2 = 3111 Bq
After 2 half-lives, the activity will be 3111 ÷ 2 = 1555.5 Bq
1555.5 = **1600 Bq (to 2 s.f.)**

[3 marks for correct answer, otherwise 1 mark for finding how many half-lives will have passed during 6 hours and 15 minutes and 1 mark for finding how many half-lives will have passed between 1 hour and 15 minutes and 6 hours and 15 minutes.]

Page 241 — Dangers of Radioactivity

Warm-up

false, false, true, false

Chapter P6

a) Source B *[1 mark]*. The chance of being contaminated by a gas is higher than a solid as it can spread out and be inhaled *[1 mark]*. Alpha radiation is most dangerous inside the body and gamma outside, so source B could cause the most damage from irradiation and contamination *[1 mark]*.

he half-life, activity and number of radioactive nuclei of each sample are ll approximately the same, so the amount of radiation being given out is pproximately the same. So the difference in risk for each source depends n the chance of being irradiated and contaminated and the type of adiation produced.

b) Second statement should be circled — Keep sources as close to you as possible at all times. *[1 mark]*. The risk of irradiation/radiation from a radioactive source increases as you get closer to the source *[1 mark]*.

Pages 242-243 — Half-life and Uses of Radiation

A *[1 mark]*

racers emit gamma radiation because it can be detected outside the body nd the source must have a relatively short half-life (of a few hours).

Ewan's statement is false. Source Y has a longer half-life, so it will initially have a lower activity than source X, and so it will be safer to be around source Y *[1 mark]*.

3 a) Beta radiation is ionising enough to kill the cells of the tumour *[1 mark]*, it also has a long enough range to reach tumour cells, but a short enough range that damage to healthy cells is limited *[1 mark]*.

b) To stop the radiation killing healthy cells once the cancerous cells have been killed *[1 mark]*.

4 How to grade your answer:

Level 0: There is no relevant information. *[No marks]*

Level 1: There is a brief description of how gamma radiation is used to kill cancer cells. *[1 to 2 marks]*

Level 2: There is a description of how gamma radiation kills cancer cells and some explanation of how the process is carried out. *[3 to 4 marks]*

Level 3: There is a detailed explanation of how the process is carried out, including how damage to healthy cells is reduced. *[5 to 6 marks]*

Here are some points your answer may include:
Gamma radiation can kill living cells, including cancer cells.
A beam of gamma rays is focused onto the tumour.
The patient stays still and the beam is rotated around them with the tumour at the centre.
Rotating the beam minimises the exposure of normal, healthy cells to radiation.
Treatment is given in doses with time gaps in between to allow healthy cells time to repair or be replaced.
The right dosage of radiation is used so the cancer cells are killed but damage to healthy cells is limited.

5 a) Iodine-123 could be injected into or swallowed by the patient, where it would be absorbed by their thyroid *[1 mark]*. The iodine would then decay, giving off radiation that could be detected outside the body *[1 mark]*. The amount of radiation detected could then be used to find how much iodine has been absorbed by the thyroid, to check whether or not the thyroid is overactive *[1 mark]*.

b) Because alpha radiation would be too dangerous inside the body *[1 mark]* and it would not be detectable outside the body, as it cannot penetrate tissue *[1 mark]*.

Chapter P6 — Matter — Models and Explanations

Pages 244-245 — Density

1 a) density = mass ÷ volume *[1 mark]*

b) density = 1.60 ÷ 0.02 = **80 kg/m³**
[2 marks for the correct answer, otherwise 1 mark for correctly substituting into the equation.]

c) volume = area × length = 0.050 × 0.40 = **0.02 m³**
mass = density × volume = 950 × 0.02 = **19 kg**
[3 marks for both correct answers, otherwise 1 mark for correct volume, 1 mark for substituting into the rearranged density equation and 1 mark for correct mass.]

2 density = mass ÷ volume
1 ml of water = 1 cm³
A: density = 5.7 ÷ 0.30 = 19 g/cm³. So A is gold.
B: density = 2.7 ÷ 0.60 = 4.5 g/cm³. So B is titanium.
C: density = 3.0 ÷ 0.30 = 10 g/cm³. So C is silver.
[5 marks for correct answer, otherwise 1 mark for using conversion 1 ml = 1 cm³, 1 mark for correct substitutions and 1 mark for each correct conclusion.]

3 How to grade your answer:

Level 0: There is no relevant information. *[No marks]*

Level 1: There is a brief explanation of how the procedure is carried out and how density is calculated. The points made are basic and not linked together. *[1 to 2 marks]*

Level 2: There is an explanation of how the procedure is carried out, and how to calculate the density from the results. Some of the points made are linked together. *[3 to 4 marks]*

Level 3: There is a detailed explanation of how the procedure is carried out and how to calculate the density from the results. The points made are well-linked and the answer has a clear and logical structure. *[5 to 6 marks]*

Here are some points your answer may include:
Measure the mass (m_1) of the object using the mass balance.
Fill the bottle with the liquid of known density.
Measure the mass of the filled bottle (m_2).
Empty the bottle and place the object being measured inside it.
Fill it with the same liquid as before.
Measure the mass of the bottle again (m_3).
Subtract the mass of the object from the new mass of the bottle, $m_4 = m_3 - m_1$.
Calculate the mass of the liquid displaced by the object by subtracting this from the mass of the bottle when it was filled with only the liquid $m = m_2 - m_4$.
Calculate the volume of the liquid displaced (which equals the volume of the object) using $V = m \div \rho$, where ρ is the density of the liquid.
The volume of liquid displaced is equal to the volume of the object.
Use this volume and the mass of the object to calculate its density.

Pages 246-247 — The Particle Model

Warm-up
From left to right: liquid, solid, gas

1 When a system is heated, the internal energy of the system <u>increases</u>. This either increases the <u>temperature</u> of the system or causes a change of state.
[2 marks — 1 mark for each correct answer]

2 a) Gas to liquid: condensing
Liquid to gas: evaporating/boiling
[1 mark for both correct]

b) E.g. a change where you don't end up with a new substance / you end up with the same substance in a different form *[1 mark]*.

c) A solid is usually more dense than a gas. *[1 mark]*

Chapter P6

3 a) E.g. there is a smaller mass (and so fewer particles) in a given volume of ice than of water ***[1 mark]***. So the water molecules are further apart in ice than they are in liquid water ***[1 mark]***.

b) The total mass stays the same ***[1 mark]*** because as the ice melts, the total number of water particles stays the same, they're just arranged differently ***[1 mark]***.

4 How to grade your answer:

Level 0: There is no relevant information. ***[No marks]***

Level 1: There is a brief description of pressure with little to no reference to the particle model. The description is basic and any points made are not linked together. No attempt is made to explain Pamela's observations. ***[1 to 2 marks]***

Level 2: There is a description of pressure in terms of the particle model. Some attempt is made to explain Pamela's observations in terms of the particle model. Some of the points made are linked together. ***[3 to 4 marks]***

Level 3: There is a detailed description of pressure in terms of the motion of particles, and a clear explanation of Pamela's observations using the particle model. The points made are well-linked and the answer has a clear and logical structure. ***[5 to 6 marks]***

Here are some points your answer may include:
Air particles move around randomly and will collide with the walls of the tyre.
Since air particles have a mass, they also have a momentum.
When an air particle collides with the wall, it will change direction and so undergo a change in momentum.
This means a force is exerted on the wall of the tyre.
The collisions of the air particles cause a net force at right angles to the walls of the tyres.
Pressure is force per unit area, so the air exerts a pressure on the tyre.
If more air is pumped into the tyre, but the volume remains constant, there will be more air particles in a given space.
This means air particles will collide with the walls of the tyre more often.
This means there is a greater net force on the tyre per unit area, and so there is an increase in pressure.
When the temperature of the tyre increases, the air particles in the tyre have more energy in their kinetic energy stores, so they travel faster.
This means their momentum also increases, so the change in momentum of the particles when they hit the tyre walls is higher.
Also, as the volume is constant, this means the particles will collide with the walls of the tyre more often.
The bigger the change in momentum, and the more often the particles hit the wall, the larger the net force on the tyre.
So there is an increase in pressure.

Page 248 — Specific Heat Capacity

Warm-up
The specific heat capacity of a substance is the energy required to increase the temperature of 1 kg of the substance by 1 °C.

1 How to grade your answer:

Level 0: There is no relevant information. ***[No marks]***

Level 1: There are only a couple of relevant points about the experiment, with no description of how to find the specific heat capacity from the results. The points made are basic and not linked together. ***[1 to 2 marks]***

Level 2: There is a brief explanation of how the experiment is carried out, and how to calculate the specific heat capacity from the results. Some of the points made are linked together. ***[3 to 4 marks]***

Level 3: There is a detailed explanation of how the experiment is carried out, including details on how to improve the accuracy of the results, and how to calculate the specific heat capacity from the results. The points made are well-linked and the answer has a clear and logical structure. ***[5 to 6 marks]***

Here are some points your answer may include:
A mass balance should be used to measure the mass of the aluminium cylinder.
The initial temperature of the aluminium should be taken.
The joulemeter should be calibrated and set to zero before the electric heater is turned on.
The thermometer should be used to measure the change in temperature of the aluminium.
Once the temperature of the aluminium has increased by a certain amount (e.g. 10 °C), the electric heater should be turned off.
The energy value on the joulemeter should be recorded once the electric heater has been turned off.
The change in thermal energy equation should then be rearranged to find specific heat capacity, and the values for the mass, temperature change and energy substituted in.
The experiment should be repeated in order to check repeatability and calculate a mean.
The accuracy could be increased by adding a lid to the cup or a conducting material/gel between the heater and cylinder.

2 Rearrange equation for change in temperature:
change in temperature
= change in thermal energy ÷ (mass × specific heat capacity)
= 302 400 ÷ (1.2 × 4200) = 60 °C
Final temperature = 24 + 60 = **84 °C**
[3 marks for correct answer, otherwise 1 mark for rearranging the equation, and 1 mark for substituting the values into the rearranged equation.]

Page 249 — Specific Latent Heat

1 a) The amount of energy required to change the state of one kilogram of a substance with no change in temperature ***[1 mark]***.

b) energy to cause a change of state = mass × specific latent heat, so specific latent heat = energy for change of state ÷ mass
specific latent heat = 1.13 ÷ 0.50 = **2.26 MJ/kg**
[3 marks for correct answer, otherwise 1 mark for correctly rearranging the equation and 1 mark for correctly substituting into the rearranged equation.]

2 a) As the bromine melts (during 3-8 minutes) ***[1 mark]***, all of the energy transferred to the substance is used to break apart intermolecular bonds ***[1 mark]*** so there is no increase in the bromine's temperature as it changes state ***[1 mark]***.

b) Melting point = –7 °C ***[1 mark]***
Boiling point = 59 °C ***[1 mark]***

Page 250 — Forces and Elasticity

Warm-up

Mixed Questions

Elastic deformation is when an object returns to its original shape or size after the deforming forces are removed *[1 mark]*. Inelastic deformation is when an object does not return to its original size or shape after the deforming forces are removed *[1 mark]*.

a) force = extension × spring constant so
spring constant = force ÷ extension
extension = 20 cm = 0.2 m
so spring constant = 250 ÷ 0.2 = **1250**
Unit = **N/m**
[5 marks for correct answer, otherwise 1 mark for recalling correct equation, 1 mark for correct rearrangement of and substitution into equation, 1 mark for correct conversion from cm to m, 1 mark for correct numerical answer and 1 mark for correct unit.]

b) E.g. Agree — the extension will be 40 cm, because force is proportional to extension, so doubling the force doubles the extension *[1 mark]*, assuming that the spring still obeys Hooke's Law *[1 mark]*.

ou could also disagree with the student's prediction here — provided you ssume that the spring will no longer obey Hooke's law when the force is oubled.

age 251 — Investigating Hooke's Law

a)

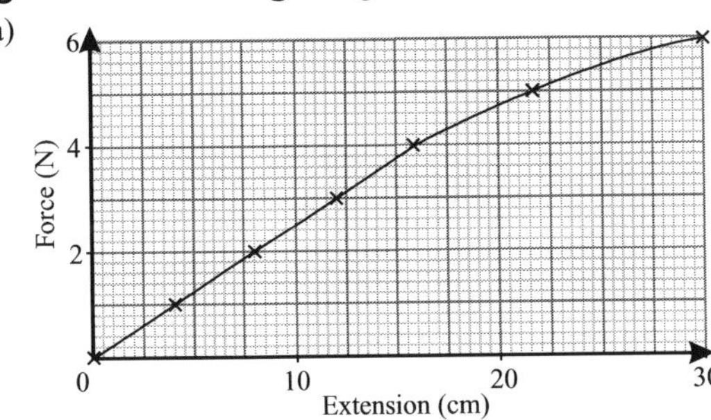

[1 mark for points plotted correctly, 1 mark for line of best fit showing linear relationship at the start, 1 mark for curved line of best fit towards the end of the graph]

b) spring constant = force ÷ extension
= gradient of the linear section of the graph
change in force = 3 – 0 = 3 N
change in extension = 12 – 0 = 12 cm = 0.12 m
spring constant = 3 ÷ 0.12 = **25 N/m**
[3 marks for correct answer between 24 and 26 N/m, otherwise 1 mark for correct method and 1 mark for converting from cm to m.]

2 Work done on spring = energy stored in a stretched spring's elastic potential energy store, so
work done = ½ × spring constant × (extension)^2
Convert extension from cm to m:
extension = 6 cm = 0.06 m
work done= ½ × 50 × 0.06^2 = **0.09 J**
[3 marks for correct answer, otherwise 1 mark for converting from cm to m and 1 mark for correctly substituting into the equation.]

Mixed Questions

Pages 252-256 — Biology Mixed Questions

1 a) i) a protein *[1 mark]*
ii) kidney *[1 mark]*
b) Enzymes speed up chemical reactions in living organisms. *[1 mark]*
c) i) 40 °C *[1 mark]*
ii) The enzyme will not work *[1 mark]* because the high temperature will change the shape of its active site/denature the enzyme *[1 mark]* and the substrate will no longer fit *[1 mark]*.

2 a) Effectors have receptors that are specific to certain hormones *[1 mark]*. Only the right hormones will bind to these receptors and have an effect *[1 mark]*.
b) Because hormones are transported round the body in the blood, which is relatively slow *[1 mark]* and the nervous response involves electrical impulses, which are very fast *[1 mark]*.
c) i) blood sugar/glucose level *[1 mark]*
ii) diabetes *[1 mark]*
d) i) LH *[1 mark]*
ii) oestrogen *[1 mark]*
e) They are inhibited by the hormones represented by lines C and D/oestrogen and progesterone *[1 mark]*.

3 a) i) A non-communicable disease because it is not transmitted between individuals/is not caused by a pathogen *[1 mark]*.
Remember, communicable diseases are caused by pathogens and can be spread between individuals. Vitamin A deficiency is caused by deficiencies in the diet, so it's non-communicable.
ii) E.g. it could make a person more susceptible to infection/communicable disease *[1 mark]* as the body would be less able to fight off infection by pathogens *[1 mark]*.
b) It will contain genes not found in normal rice / DNA from a bacterium and a maize plant *[1 mark]*.
c) E.g. the genes to be used from the maize plant and the soil bacterium were isolated and replicated/copied *[1 mark]*. The copies were then inserted into vectors *[1 mark]*. The vectors were then inserted into the cells of (embryonic) rice plants *[1 mark]* and plants that had taken up the vectors containing the desired genes were selected to produce Golden Rice *[1 mark]*.

4 a) i) Tube 1 *[1 mark]*
ii) Tube 1 shows that in the dark, the algae are producing more carbon dioxide than they take in *[1 mark]*. The concentration of carbon dioxide is high because the cells are respiring, but not photosynthesising (as there's no light for photosynthesis to take place) *[1 mark]*. Tube 2 shows that in the light, the algae are taking up more carbon dioxide than they produce *[1 mark]*. The concentration of carbon dioxide has reduced because the cells are photosynthesising faster than they are respiring *[1 mark]*.
Plant cells respire all the time but they can only photosynthesise when it's light.
iii) Any two from: e.g. the temperature of the boiling tubes / the volume of hydrogencarbonate indicator / the concentration of hydrogencarbonate indicator / the number of beads in each tube / the concentration of algal cells in each bead ***[2 marks — 1 mark for each correct answer]***.
b) i) Light intensity *[1 mark]* because the rate of photosynthesis is increasing as the light intensity increases *[1 mark]*.
ii) carbon dioxide concentration [1 mark]

Pages 257-262 — Chemistry Mixed Questions

1 a)

Br Br

[1 mark for shared pair of electrons, 1 mark for six further electrons in the outer shell of each bromine atom.]
b) simple molecular substance *[1 mark]*
c) liquid *[1 mark]*

Mixed Questions

2 a) i) E.g. burning of sulfur impurities in fossil fuels ***[1 mark for a valid source of SO_2 pollution]***.

ii) SO_2 mixes with clouds to form sulfuric acid, causing acid rain ***[1 mark]***.

b) $2SO_2 + O_2 \rightleftharpoons 2SO_3$

[2 marks for all formulas correct and a correctly-balanced equation, otherwise 1 mark for correct formulas in an unbalanced equation.]

3 a) Polymer A has weak forces between the chains ***[1 mark]***. Polymer B has crosslinks between the chains ***[1 mark]***.

b) Polymer B ***[1 mark]*** as it's rigid, so would keep the shape of the mug ***[1 mark]***, and it wouldn't be softened by the hot drinks ***[1 mark]***.

4 a) $2Rb_{(s)} + F_{2(g)} \rightarrow 2RbF_{(s)}$

[1 mark for all formulas correct, 1 mark for a correctly balanced equation and 1 mark for correct state symbols.]

b) ionic bonding ***[1 mark]***

c) The products are at a lower energy than the reactants ***[1 mark]***.

d) 2.7 ***[1 mark]***

5 a) $2Al + 6H^+ \rightarrow 3H_2 + 2Al^{3+}$ ***[1 mark for all formulas correct, 1 mark for correct balancing.]***

b) Hold a lit splint at the open end of a test tube containing the gas ***[1 mark]***. If hydrogen is present, you will hear a squeaky pop ***[1 mark]***.

c) E.g. add a set volume and concentration of sulfuric acid to the reaction vessel ***[1 mark]***. Add a set mass of aluminium ***[1 mark]***, connect the reaction flask to a gas syringe ***[1 mark]*** and start the stopwatch ***[1 mark]***. Record the volume of gas collected at regular intervals until the reaction is finished ***[1 mark]***. Repeat the experiment, keeping everything the same except for the concentration of acid ***[1 mark]***.

d) Change in volume = 12.0 cm³

Mean rate of reaction = $\frac{\text{amount of product formed}}{\text{time}} = \frac{12.0}{30}$

= **0.40 cm³/s** ***[2 marks for a correct answer, otherwise 1 mark for using the correct equation to calculate rate.]***

e) 64 aluminium cubes, each with side length 2 cm ***[1 mark]***.

The smaller cubes will give the highest rate of reaction, as they have the greatest surface area to volume ratio.

6 a)

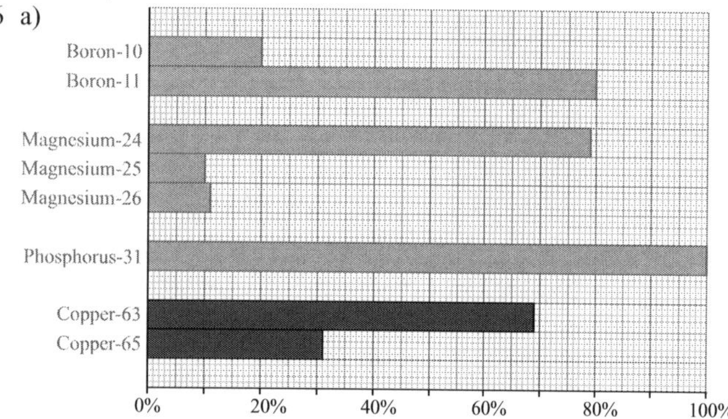

[1 mark for each correct bar.]

b) The relative atomic mass of an element is the average of the mass numbers of all the atoms of that element ***[1 mark]***. Phosphorus only has one isotope, so its relative atomic mass is equal to the mass number of its atoms (31) ***[1 mark]***. Boron, magnesium and copper all have more than one isotope, which exist in different quantities, so the average of their mass numbers won't be a whole number ***[1 mark]***.

c) % Mg-24 = 79%, % Mg-25 = 10%, % Mg-26 = 11%

So, relative atomic mass of Mg =

[(24.0 × 79) + (25.0 × 10) + (26.0 × 11)] ÷ 100

= 2432 ÷ 100 = **24.3**

[3 marks for a correct answer correctly rounded to 3 s.f. Otherwise 1 mark for correct % abundances of Mg isotopes and 1 mark for correctly substituting the atomic masses and abundances into an equation to work out relative atomic mass.]

d) The atomic number is equal to the number of electrons in an atom ***[1 mark]***, and 2+ ions are formed when the atom loses 2 electrons, so a Cu^{2+} ion contains 29 – 2 = **27** electrons ***[1 mark]***.

7 a) E.g. carbon monoxide [1 mark]

b) $ZnSO_4$ [1 mark]

c) It is more reactive than carbon [1 mark] and so cannot be reduced by carbon [1 mark].

8 a) $BaCl_2$**(aq)** + $2AgNO_3$**(aq)** → $2AgCl$**(s)** + $Ba(NO_3)_2$**(aq)** ***[1 mark]***

b) i) Crystallisation is used to separate soluble solids from solutions [1 mark]. Silver chloride is an insoluble solid so cannot be crystallised ***[1 mark]***.

ii) filtration [1 mark]

c) Representative samples are samples taken at random from the substance you are testing ***[1 mark]***. Taking representative samples accounts for any variation in the composition of the substance ***[1 mark]***.

9 a) i) cubic

ii) hexagonal [1 mark for parts i) and ii) both correct]

b) Each atom is bonded to four other atoms with strong covalent bonds [1 mark], which makes crystals of cubic boron nitride very rigid/hard [1 mark].

c) The sheets of hexagonal boron nitride are held together by very weak forces [1 mark] so the layers are very slippery because they can slide easily over each other [1 mark].

d) Hexagonal boron nitride does not contain any delocalised electrons [1 mark].

Pages 263-268 — Physics Mixed Questions

1 a) Convert time to seconds:

time = 5 × 60 = 300 s

average speed = distance ÷ time = 420 ÷ 300 = **1.4 m/s**

[4 marks for correct answer, otherwise 1 mark for converting time to seconds, 1 mark for stating the equation for average speed and 1 mark for correct substitution.]

b) her speed ***[1 mark]***

c) mechanically ***[1 mark]***

2 a) A permanent magnet produces its own magnetic field ***[1 mark]***. An induced magnet is a material that only produces a magnetic field when it is in an external magnetic field ***[1 mark]***.

b) It is a repulsive non-contact force ***[1 mark]***.

3 a) After 1 half-life: 7640 ÷ 2 = 3820 Bq

After 2 half-lives: 3820 ÷ 2 = 1910 Bq

So there are 2 half-lives in 16 days, so:

half-life = 16 ÷ 2 = **8 days**

[2 marks for the correct answer, otherwise 1 mark for calculating the number of half-lives.]

b) Sam is correct because alpha particles are blocked by the lead lining ***[1 mark]*** but gamma rays can pass through and reach the detector ***[1 mark]***.

4 a) Rearrange power = (current)² × resistance for resistance:

resistance = power ÷ (current)²

resistance = 0.4 ÷ 2.0² = 0.4 ÷ 4.0 = **0.1 Ω**

[4 marks for the correct answer, otherwise 1 mark for stating the correct equation, 1 mark for correct rearrangement and 1 mark for correct substitution.]

Mixed Questions

b) Convert length from cm to m:
length = 10 ÷ 100 = 0.1 m
force = magnetic flux density × current × length of conductor
force = 0.065 × 2.0 × 0.1 = **0.013 N**
[3 marks for correct answer, otherwise 1 mark for converting from cm to m and 1 mark for correct substitution.]

a)

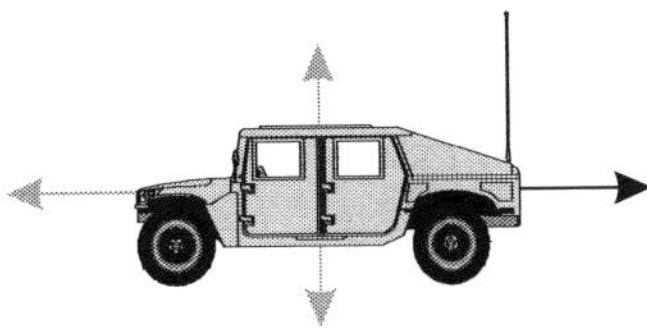

[1 mark for an arrow in the right direction and 1 mark for it being the same length as the driving force arrow.]

b) Efficiency = useful energy transferred ÷ total energy transferred ***[1 mark]***

c) 65% = 0.65
Useful energy transferred = efficiency × total energy transferred
= 0.65 × 1200
= **780 J**
[3 marks for correct answer, otherwise 1 mark for correct rearrangement and 1 mark for correct substitution.]

d) E.g. energy is transferred electrically ***[1 mark]*** from the chemical energy store of the battery to the kinetic energy store of the motor ***[1 mark]***. Energy is transferred mechanically ***[1 mark]*** from the kinetic energy store of the motor to the kinetic energy stores of the wheels / to the kinetic energy store of the toy car ***[1 mark]***. Some energy is dissipated to the surroundings by sound / by heating due to friction ***[1 mark]***.

First, calculate the energy transferred for the water to reach its freezing point:
Change in temperature = 20 °C – 0 °C = 20 °C
200 g = 0.2 kg
Change in internal energy
= mass × specific heat capacity × change in temperature
= 0.2 × 4200 × 20 = 16 800 J
Now calculate the energy transferred as the water changes state:
Energy to cause a change of state
= mass × specific latent heat
= 0.2 × 330 000 = 66 000 J
Now add together these two energies:
16 800 + 66 000 = 82 800
= **83 000 J (to 2 s.f.)**
[5 marks for correct answer, otherwise 1 mark for correct conversions of mass to kg, 1 mark for calculating the energy transferred away whilst cooling to 0°C, 1 mark for calculating energy transferred away whilst freezing, 1 mark for adding the two energies together and 1 mark for giving answer to 2 s.f.]

7 a) The surface temperature of star B is higher than that of star A ***[1 mark]*** because the peak/principal wavelength is lower for star B than for star A ***[1 mark]***.

b) The telescope must be in space, because ultraviolet waves will be absorbed by oxygen in the atmosphere (forming ozone) and would not reach a telescope on the Earth's surface ***[1 mark]***.

8 a) E.g.

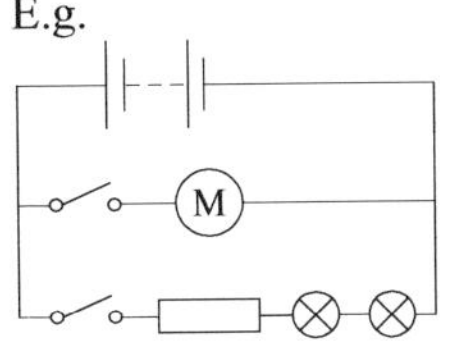

[2 marks for all circuit symbols correctly drawn, otherwise 1 mark for 4 symbols correctly drawn. 1 mark for filament lamps and resistor in series with each other, 1 mark for motor in parallel with other components and 1 mark for correct placement of switches.]

b) First, calculate the power of the motor:
power = potential difference × current
Convert current to amperes:
current = 70.0 ÷ 1000 = 0.07 A
power = 6.0 × 0.07 = 0.42 W
Next calculate total energy transferred to the motor:
energy transferred = power × time,
Convert time to seconds:
time = 15 × 60 = 900 s
energy transferred = 0.42 × 900 = 378 J
Then calculate the energy transferred to heat the casing:
change in internal energy
= mass × specific heat capacity × change in temperature
= 0.0250 × 120 × 6.0 = 18 J
Subtract the wasted energy from the total energy transferred.
useful energy transferred = 378 – 18 = **360 J**
[5 marks for the correct answer, otherwise 1 mark for converting current into amperes and time into seconds, 1 mark for calculating the power, 1 mark for calculating the energy transferred and 1 mark for calculating the wasted energy.]

c) He could lubricate the parts within the motor ***[1 mark]***. This would reduce friction and the amount of energy being wasted/dissipated to the thermal energy store of the motor ***[1 mark]***.

9 a) density = mass ÷ volume, so
mass = density × volume
= 1.21 × 4.2 = 5.082 g = **5.1 g (to 2 s.f.)**
[4 marks for correct answer, otherwise 1 mark for recalling and correctly rearranging the equation for density, 1 mark for correct substitution, 1 mark for correct numerical answer and 1 mark for correctly rounding your answer to 2 s.f.]

b) i) Find the acceleration of the marble.
Marble B goes from rest (0 m/s) to 7.75 m/s in 1.55 s, so
acceleration = change in speed ÷ time
= (7.75 – 0) ÷ 1.55
= 5.0 m/s ***[1 mark]***
force = mass × acceleration ***[1 mark]***
rearrange for mass
mass = force ÷ acceleration
= 0.0570 ÷ 5.0 ***[1 mark]***
= 0.0114 kg ***[1 mark]***
convert mass to grams
mass = 0.0114 × 1000 = **11.4 g** ***[1 mark]***

You could also have done this by finding the change of momentum of the marble, and using change of momentum = resultant force × time for which it acts.

ii) density = mass ÷ volume = 11.4 ÷ 4.2
= 2.714... g/cm^3
From the table: the marble is made of **glass**.
[2 marks for correct answer, otherwise 1 mark for the correct substitution into the density equation.]

ISBN 978 1 78294 513 0
9 781782 945130

S2HQA41 £2.00 (Retail Price)

www.cgpbooks.co.uk